Singing Fun

by

LUCILLE F. WOOD
Associate Professor of Music
California State College at Los Angeles

and

LOUISE B. SCOTT
Associate Professor of Elementary Speech
California State College at Los Angeles

miller

WEBSTER DIVISION, McGRAW-HILL BOOK COMPANY
St. Louis · New York · San Francisco · Dallas · Toronto · London

Acknowledgments

For their help and suggestions in arranging *Singing Fun,* the authors wish to express appreciation to the following people.

Dr. Gladys Tipton, Professor of Music Education, Teachers College, Columbia University

Mrs. Kathryn Barnard, Vocal Instructor (retired), Pasadena City College

Mrs. Roberta McLaughlin, Music Consultant, Los Angeles County

Miss Muriel Dawley, Music Consultant, Los Angeles County

Thanks are extended to Mrs. Agnes Frye, Consultant in Speech Education, California State Department of Education, for introducing the songs into speech activity.

The authors wish to thank the following publisher for permission to use copyrighted material in this book.

Milton Bradley Company for use of "Green Frog" and "The Owl and the Brownies" from *Rhymes for Little Hands* by Maude Burnham

55820

567890—BABA—754321069

I'll Make a Scarecrow

L. F. W.

L. F. W.

Gaily

G D7 G D7 G

I'll take my dad - dy's coat, I'll take my dad - dy's hat, And I'll make a scare - crow just like that!

It's Fall

Autumn days are on their way.
Pretty leaves are bright and gay.
Summer's over; nights are cool.
Boys and girls are back at school.
Halloween, Thanksgiving time
Give us words that we can rhyme.
Scarecrows, witches, pumpkins bring
Many songs we like to sing.

Falling Leaves

L. B. S.

Traditional

Slowly and smoothly

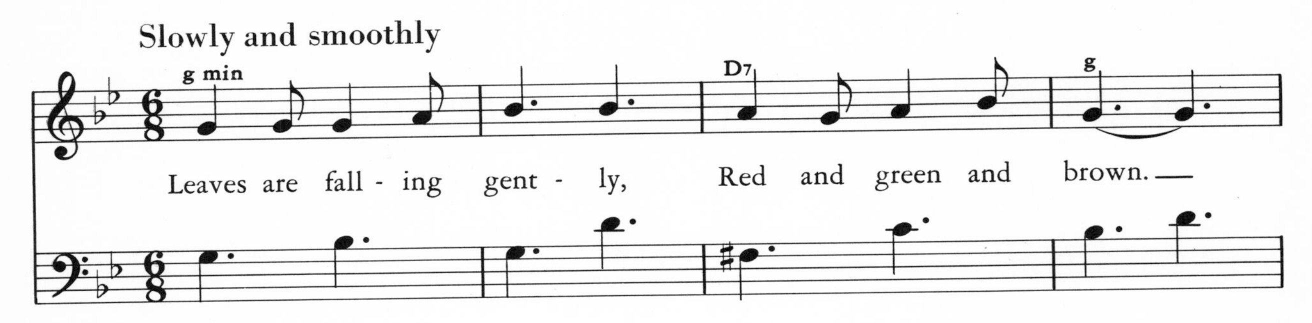

g min
D7
g
Leaves are fall - ing gent - ly, Red and green and brown.

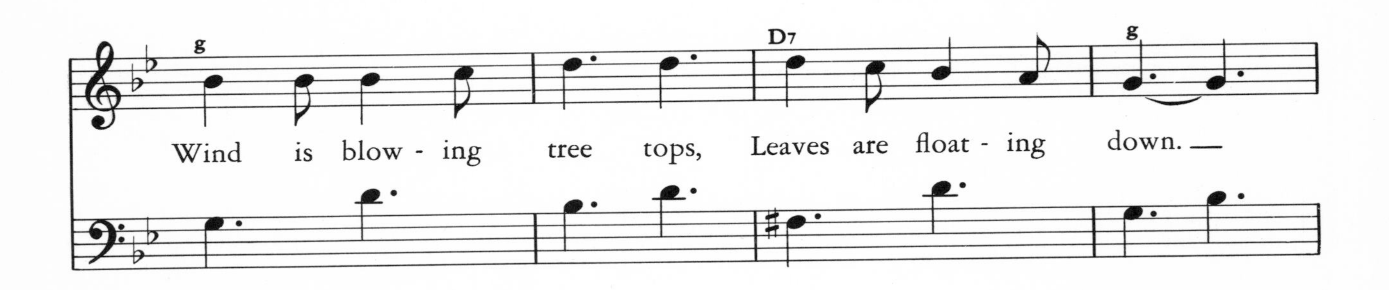

g
D7
g
Wind is blow - ing tree tops, Leaves are float - ing down.

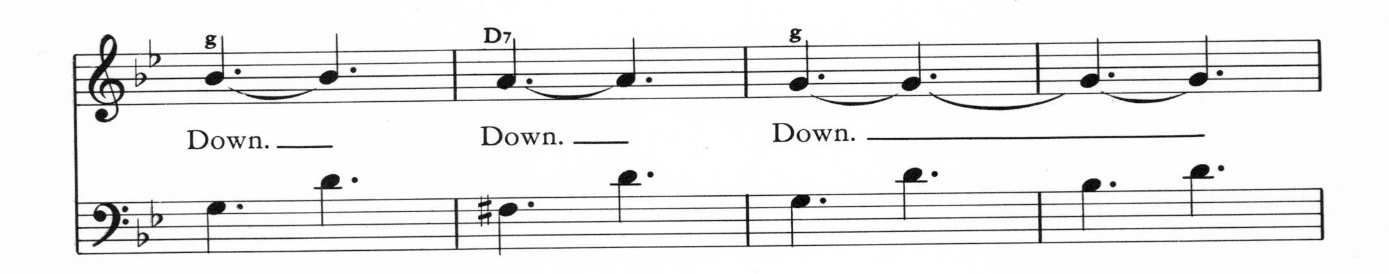

g
D7
g
Down. Down. Down.

g
D7
g
Down. Down. Down.

Someday the children may want to sing about the rain or snow falling. If they rub their palms together it will sound like softly falling rain.

The Owl and The Brownies

Maude Burnham

L. F. W.

Mysteriously
An owl sat a - lone on the branch of a tree, And
Some brown - ies crept up on the branch of the tree, And
he was as qui - et as qui - et could be. His
they were as qui - et as qui - et could be. Said the
eyes were o - pen and round like this. He
wise old owl, "Too whoo, Too whoo!" Then
looked all a - round; not a thing did he miss.
up jumped the brown - ies and a - way they flew!

The Scarecrow

L. B. S. | L. F. W.

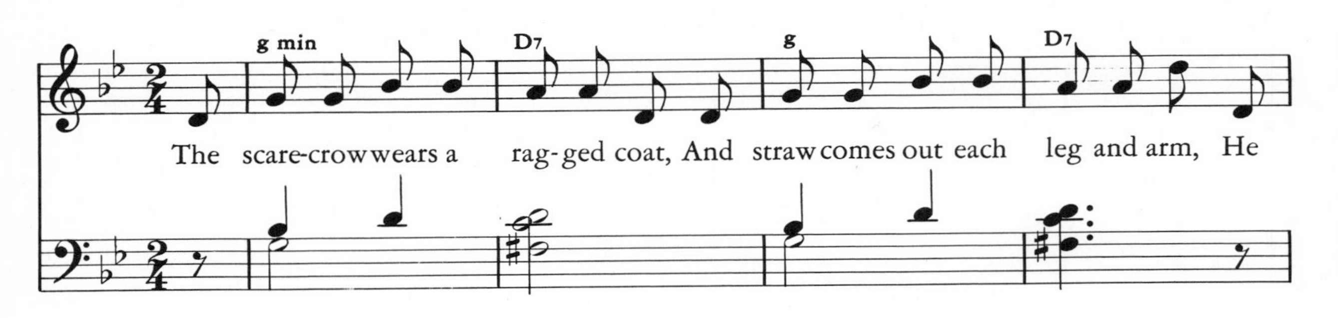
g min D7 g D7
The scare-crow wears a rag-ged coat, And straw comes out each leg and arm, He

g D7 g
has a fun - ny flop - py hat, He lives down on the farm. The

D7 g D7
scare crow is a fun - ny man, And when the wind be - gins to blow, He

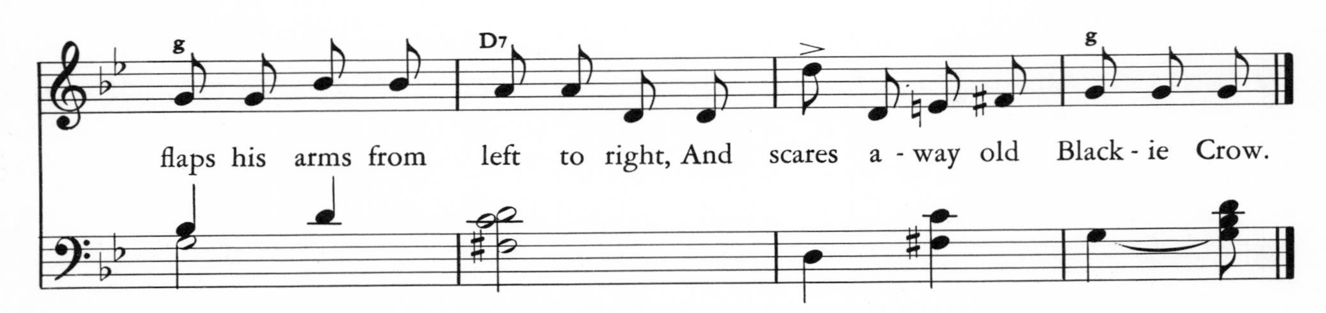
g D7 g
flaps his arms from left to right, And scares a - way old Black - ie Crow.

Gregory visited a farm in Iowa last summer. He showed us how the scarecrow's arms dangled and flopped.

Sometimes we all play scarecrows. Sometimes we have one scarecrow who sends all the crows flying out the door when the bell rings!

Little Jackie Jack Frost

L. F. W.
L. F. W.
Gaily
F
C7
Lit - tle Jack - ie Jack Frost bites my nose,
Lit - tle Jack - ie Jack Frost thinks it's fun,
F
Lit - tle Jack - ie Jack Frost stings my toes,
Knock - ing all the leaves down one by one,
F
C7
Lit - tle Jack - ie Jack Frost climbs the trees,
When the win - ter wind be - gins to blow,
C7
F
Lit - tle Jack - ie Jack Frost paints the leaves.
Lit - tle Jack - ie runs a - way Ho! Ho!

Halloween Fun

Halloween is on its way—
Smiling jack-o'-lanterns gay,
Witches in tall pointed hats,
Ghosts and goblins, big black cats,
Hoot owls with round, yellow eyes,
Whistling noises, moans and sighs—
All these eerie sights are seen.
Come, let's sing of Halloween!

Three Little Pumpkins

Ruthelma Hemstead

Ruthelma Hemstead

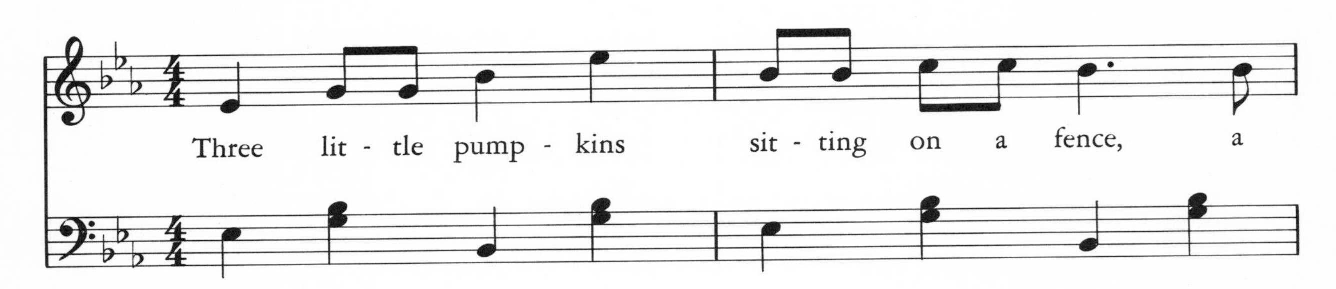
Three lit - tle pump - kins sit - ting on a fence, a

witch came rid - ing by, Ha! Ha! Ha! I'll

take you all, And make a pump - kin pie. Ha! Ha!

Halloween's Coming

*A THIRD GRADE
*A THIRD GRADE
Mysteriously
Hal-low-een's com - ing, Hal-low-een's com - ing, Skel - e - tons will be
af - ter you; Witch-es, cats, and big black bats, Ghosts and gob - lins, too!
Flap, flap, flap, go the big black bats, Oooooooooooooooooooooooooooo!
"Meow, Meow, Meow," say the ug - ly cats, Ooooooooooooooooooo! BOO!

*Teacher: Esther Alkire Getts

A third grade had fun composing this song. All children enjoy creating spooky words and tunes.

I Made a Jack-O'-Lantern

Unknown

L. F. W.

Lightly and gaily

I made a jack - o' - lan - tern; I made him yes - ter - day. I

made two eyes like big, round wheels; I made his nose this way. I

made his mouth in - to a smile With ev - 'ry tooth in place, And

then a can - dle light ed up My jack - o' - lan - tern's face!

Children will enjoy finding motions to go with this song.

In a Pumpkin Patch

L. B. S.
L. F. W.
G
D7
1&5 Three lit - tle pump - kins ly - ing ve - ry still In a
pump - kin patch on a great big hill.
G D7 G
Fine
G (3 times)
2. This one said, "Oh, I'm ve - ry, ve - ry green; But
3. This one said, "Oh, — me! — Oh, — my! To
4. This one said, "Oh, — I am on my way To
D7
G D7 G
D.C.
I'll be orange for Hal - low - e'en."
day I'll be a pump - kin pie."
be a Jack - o' - lan - tern gay."

Children think it fun to act out this song and sing the parts individually.

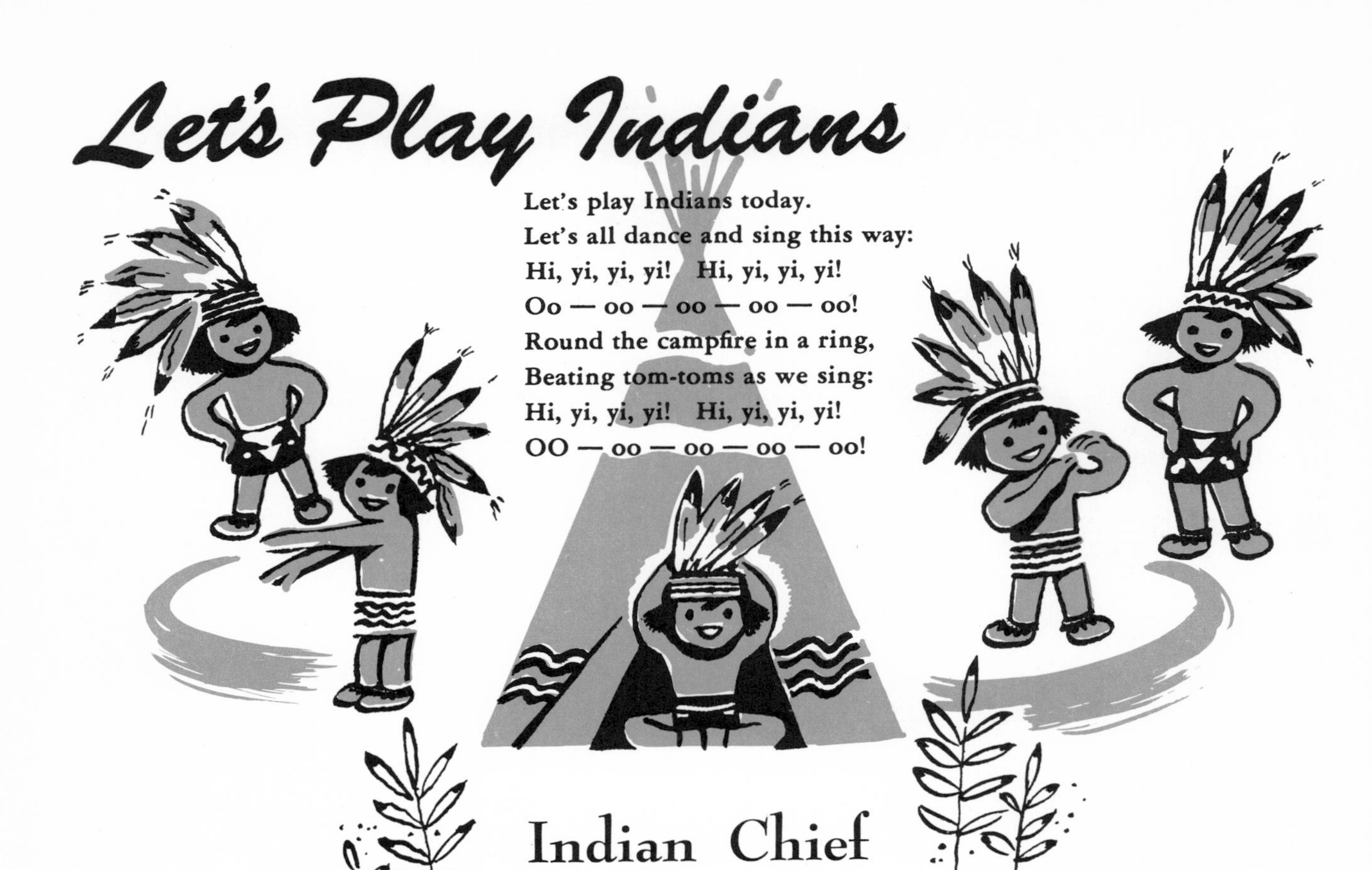
Let's Play Indians
Let's play Indians today.
Let's all dance and sing this way:
Hi, yi, yi, yi! Hi, yi, yi, yi!
Oo — oo — oo — oo — oo!
Round the campfire in a ring,
Beating tom-toms as we sing:
Hi, yi, yi, yi! Hi, yi, yi, yi!
OO — oo — oo — oo — oo!

Indian Chief

L. B. S. L. F. W.

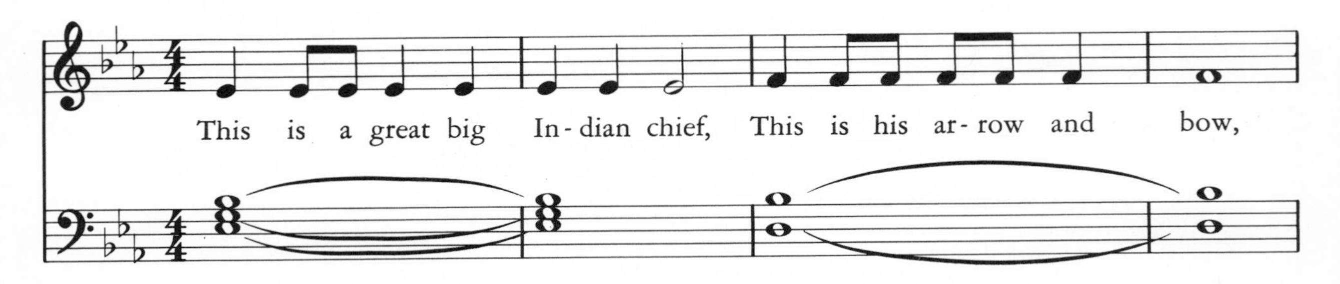
This is a great big In-dian chief, This is his ar-row and bow,

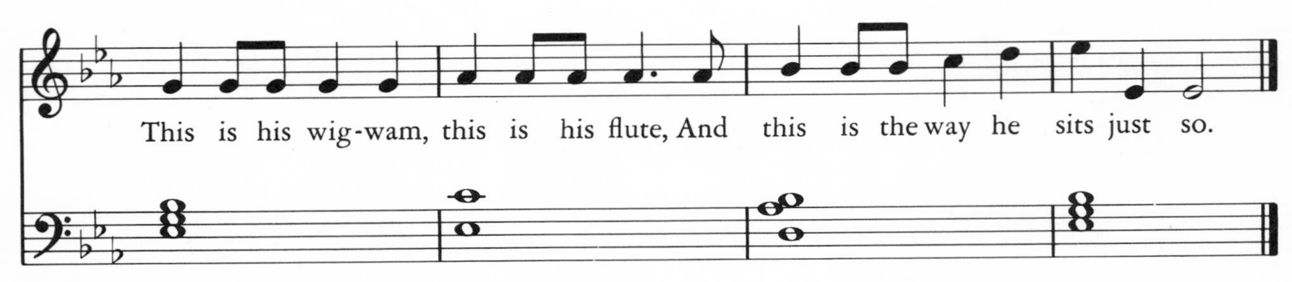
This is his wig-wam, this is his flute, And this is the way he sits just so.

Indian songs, like Halloween songs, are fun to compose. Children may add verses about other Indian activities. Here is a verse that fits the tune of the "Indian Chief."

I am a little Indian boy, My name is Rising Sun.
I like to paddle my birch canoe, And riding my pony is lots of fun.

Indians In a Teepee

L. F. W.
L. B. S.
d min
Five lit - tle In - dians in a tee - pee,
Sleep - ing qui - et - ly as can be. A - long comes the chief and
A7
d
what do you think? Up jump the In - dians Quick as a wink!
A7
d

How Many Feathers?

L. B. S. L. B. S.

Gaily
How man - y feath - ers ___ would you say? How man - y do I
Tell me ___ what will the col - ors be For an ___ In - dian

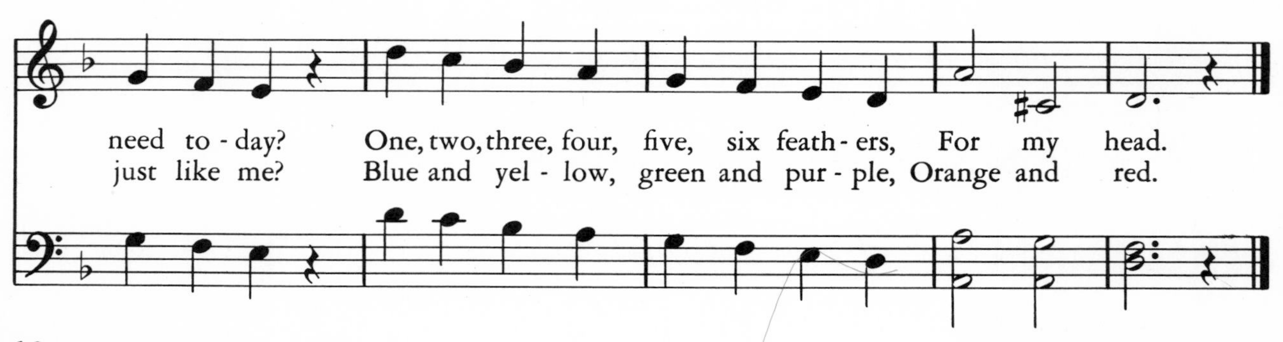
need to - day? One, two, three, four, five, six feath - ers, For my head.
just like me? Blue and yel - low, green and pur - ple, Orange and red.

Indians

L. B. S.
L. F. W.
With marked accent
An In - dian wears a buck - skin suit, Tom, tom, tom! Tom, tom, tom! He
some-times plays a lit - tle flute, Too, too, too! Too, too, too! I'd
8va
like to live as In - dians do, And wear some feath - ers red and blue.
Tom, tom, tom! Tom, tom, tom! Too, too, too! Too, too, too!
8va

Joy: "I can play the tom-toms and the too-toos on the piano. Shall I play them while you sing?"

Thanksgiving Time

Thank You for the world so sweet;
Thank You for the food we eat;
Thank You for the birds that sing;
Thank You, God, for everything.

—An English Grace

Little Pilgrims

L. B. S. — L. F. W.

Not too fast
G
D7
Wake up, lit - tle pil - grims; the sun is in the east, To
The tur - key is roast - ing; the pies are gold - en brown; The
And now to the ta - ble, but first we say a prayer: We
G D7 G
day is the day of our Thanks - giv - ing feast.
peo - ple are gath - 'ring from all the coun - try round.
thank Thee for food and ___ for Thy lov - ing care.

A Thankgiving Prayer

L. F. W. L. F. W.

Slowly and quietly
1&4. Two lit - tle chil - dren on Thanks - giv - ing Day

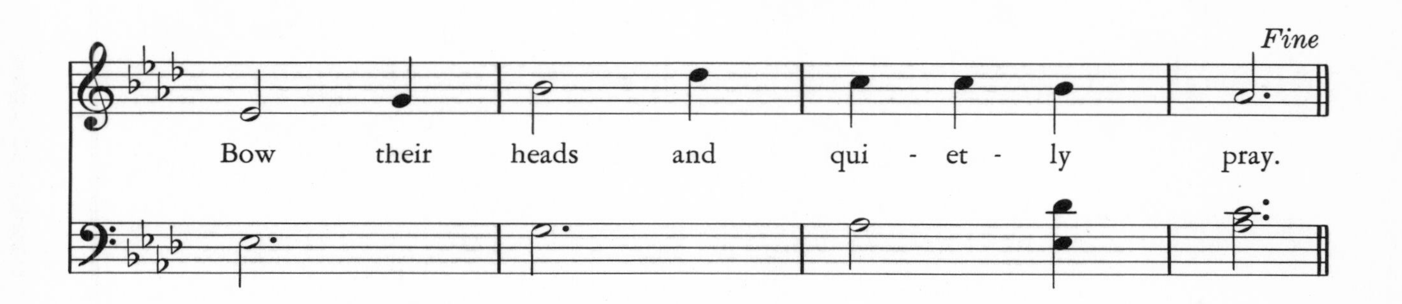
Fine
Bow their heads and qui - et - ly pray.

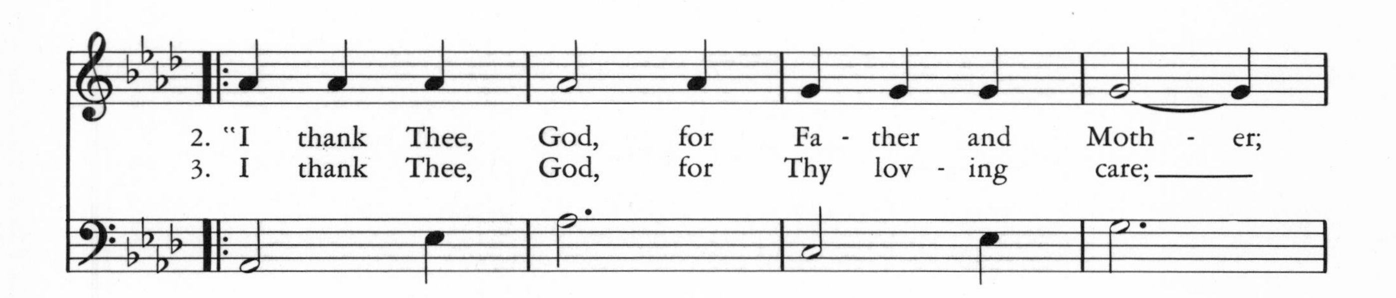
2. "I thank Thee, God, for Fa - ther and Moth - er;
3. I thank Thee, God, for Thy lov - ing care;

D.C.
Teach us to love and help each oth - er.
Teach us to give and how to share."

Children will like to make other verses about things for which they are thankful.

Foolish Question

L. B. S. | L. F. W.

Lightly

F | C7

I met a Tur-key Gob - bler When I went out to play. Oh,

F

Mis - ter Tur - key Gob - bler, How are you to - day?

C7

Gob - ble, Gob - ble, Gob - ble, That I can - not say. Don't

F

ask me such a ques - tion on Thanks - giv - ing Day!

Three Turkeys

L. F. W. L. F. W.

F
C7
1. The night be - fore Thanks-giv - ing When — I had gone to bed I
5. Then on Thanks-giv - ing morn - ing When the farm - er came a - round Those
F
Fine
heard three tur - key gob - blers, and this is what they said.
three — tur - key gob - blers could — not be found.
(3 times)
F
C7
2. The first — tur - key said, "I think that I will go And
3. The sec - ond tur - key said, "I think I'll find a tree And
4. The third — tur - key said, "I think it would be fun To
F
D.C.
hide be - hind the hay - stack Where no one will know."
hide up in the branch - es Where no one will see."
hide the farm - er's hatch - et, Then run, run, run, run."

The words of this song suggest dramatization. The children will find appropriate spots for the haystack, the tree, and a place to hide the hatchet!

It's Winter

Ooooooo—oooooooo!
The North Wind blows.
It stirs up the leaves,
It piles up the snow,
It rattles the windows,
It howls and moans,
It sways the treetops,
It whistles and groans.
Ooooooo—oooooooo!
Ooooooo—oooooooo!
Ooooooo—oooooooo!

The Snowman

L. B. S.
L. F. W.
Two swings to a measure
Here is a snow-man big and white, Is-n't he a fun-ny sight!
Let's make a snow-ball, Toss it at his hat, Off it goes, Just like that!

I Am a Pine Tree

L. B. S. L. B. S.

Swaying rhythm

F C7
I am a pine tree stand - ing on a hill.

F C7 F
I can stand so ve - ry, ve - ry still.

B♭ F
All at once the wind be - gins to blow.

C7 F C7 F C7 F
I bend to and fro, to and fro, to and fro.

This is an effective relaxation song.

Walking Weather

L. F. W.
Kathryn Franks
C G7
When it rains I walk a - long, I splash through pud - dles and
sum - mer days in noon day heat, I walk a - long with
C G7 C
whis - tle a song. (Whistle)
la - zy feet. (Whistle slowly) On
G7
When the snow falls on the ground I like the way my
wind - y days I think it's fun to take a deep breath and
1. C
snow shoes sound. On
2. C 3 3
run run run run run run run.
(Quickly)

Funny Little Snowman

L. B. S.
L. F. W.
Lightly
1. Fun - ny lit - tle snow - man, Round and fat,
2. Fun - ny lit - tle snow - man Smiles all day
3. Fun - ny lit - tle snow - man See the sun,
With your eyes of coal and your stove - pipe hat!
When the wind is cold and the skies are gray.
Quick, — lit - tle snow - man! Oh, run, run, run.

Snowflakes

L. F. W

L. F. W

Gracefully

From dark gray clouds up in the sky, Snow-flakes fall

soft - ly down, down, down. ——— Then the

cold, cold wind comes whist - ling by, And the snow-flakes whirl

swift - ly round, round, round. ——— See!

When given the opportunity, children will move rhythmically to portray floating flakes or whirling wind.

I can reach al - most as high As those

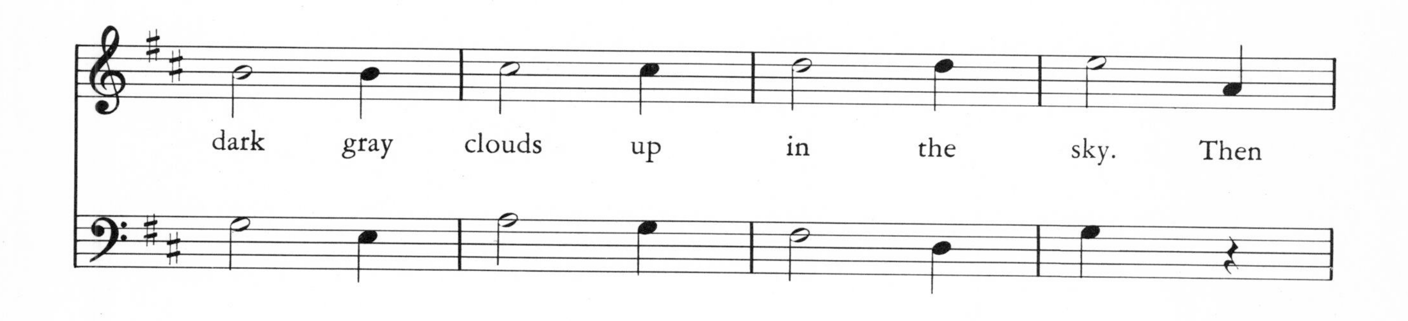
dark gray clouds up in the sky. Then

like the snow - flakes soft and white I float to the

earth a - gain, down, down, down.

Ten Little Jingle Bells

Virginia Pavelko

Virginia Pavelko

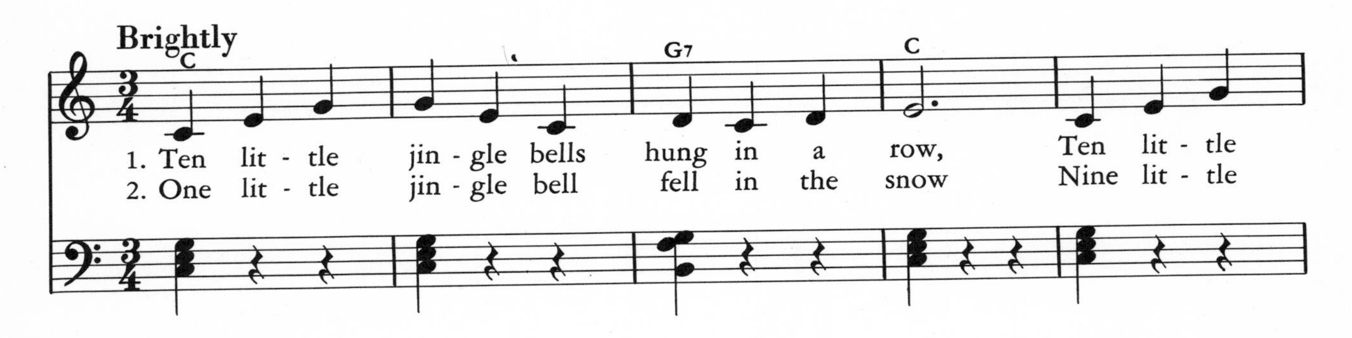
Brightly
C
G7
C
1. Ten lit - tle jin - gle bells hung in a row, Ten lit - tle
2. One lit - tle jin - gle bell fell in the snow Nine lit - tle

G7
C
Chorus:
C
jin - gle bells helped the horse go. Mer - ri - ly mer - ri - ly
jin - gle bells helped the horse go.

G7
C
G7
C
o - ver the snow, Mer - ri - ly, mer - ri - ly sleigh - ing we go.

Last verse slowly:

One little jingle bell fell in the snow,
No little jingle bells help the horse go.
Slowly, so slowly the bells are all gone.
We'll get some new ones and put them right on.

Original Chorus: Brightly

Christmas Time

Johnny sang of Christmas trees
Trimmed in tinsel gay.
Bobby sang of Santa Claus,
His reindeer, and his sleigh.
Billy sang of the Christ Child
Born so long ago.

Tommy sang of a fireplace
And stockings in a row.
Dickie sang of presents
Piled beneath a tree.
You, too, can sing if you will
Make some words and tunes with me.

—J. J. Thompson

Magic Time

L. B. S. | L. F. W.

Merrily, with a running rhythm
On Christ - mas Eve does San - ta pack A mil - lion toys in - side his sack? Oh, yes, it's so! Oh, yes, it's so! It is a mag - ic time, you know.
On Christ - mas Eve can rein - deer fly To car - ry San - ta through the sky? Oh, yes, it's so! Oh, yes, it's so! It is a mag - ic time, you know.
On Christ - mas Eve does San - ta creep Right down the chim - ney while I sleep? Oh, yes, it's so! Oh, yes, it's so! It is a mag - ic time, you know.

On question and answer songs, children like to sing in groups.

Christmas Tree Angel

L. B. S.
L. F. W.
Tenderly
An - gel on top of the Christ - mas tree with
ha - lo and wings so bright,
Guard - ing me now as I go to sleep, As you
guard - ed the Christ Child on Christ - mas night.

When the teacher played these chords in arpeggio style in the upper register of the piano, Barbara said, "That sounded like *angel* music."

On a Christmas Night

L. B. S.
L. F. W.
Smoothly
On a love - ly Christ-mas night Shep-herds trav - eled far,
Seek- ing Ba - by Je - sus, Fol - low - ing a star.
Shep-herds came to Beth - le - hem, Heard the an - gels sing,
Found a lit - tle man - ger And the new born King!

A happy custom at one of our schools is to invite the fathers of the kindergarten children to come at 7 a.m. on the Friday before Christmas vacation. The children play and sing their Christmas music and serve coffee and doughnuts to their fathers.

Santa's Reindeer

L. B. S.
L. F. W.
Galloping rhythm
G
D7
Some Christ-mas Eve I'd like to go with San - ta in his sleigh ___ To
G
drive the rein - deer o'er the snow, and this is what I'd say, ___ "On,
D7
Dash - er, Dan - cer, Pran - cer, Ho! Vix - en, Com - et, too; ___ On
G
Cup - id, Don - der, Blit - zen!" Oh! That's what I would do. ___

Rhythm bells and coconut shells make this song more fun.

Easter Bunny

L. B. S.

L. F. W.

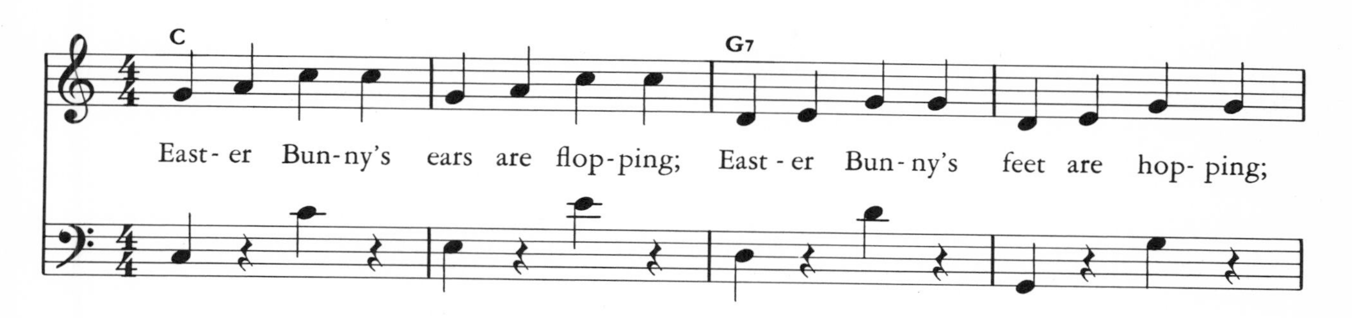
C
G7
East- er Bun-ny's ears are flop-ping; East - er Bun-ny's feet are hop- ping;

C
F
G7
C
Nose is soft and fur is fluff - y; Tail is short and pow-der puff - y.

It's Spring

I like to sing about the spring.
It rhymes with ring and wing and swing,
And blossoming and caroling,
And gardening and evening.
It is more fun than anything
To make a song about the spring.

A Green Frog

Maude Burnham

L. B. S.

g min
D7
On the edge of a pond on a great big log Sat
g
D7
pa - tient - ly wait - ing a speck - led green frog. He
g
D7
g
D7
winked, and he blinked, and he rolled each eye; Then
g
SNAP went the frog at a lit - tle green fly!

My Easter Bonnet

Helen Wasmansdorff
L. F. W.
I think I'll wear for East - er A bon - net made of lace. But
most of all I think I'll wear a smile up - on my face. A
smile up - on your face? A smile up - on your face? I
think I'll like that bet - ter than your bon - net made of lace.

Pussy Willow

Traditional

C
G
I know a lit - tle pus - sy, Her coat is sil - ver gray. She
C
G
lives down in the meadow Not ve - ry far a - way. Al -
C
F
though she is a pus - sy, She'll nev - er be a cat, For
G7
C
she's a pus - sy wil - low. Now what do you think of that? Meow,
meow, meow, meow, meow, meow, meow, meow!
SCAT!

Pussy Willow has long been our favorite spring song. It's fun to start the song in a crouched position, gradually rising with the tune, down again on the *meows*, and up on the *scat!*

Little Seeds

L. B. S.
L. F. W.
Smoothly
d min
A7
d
Seeds are bur - ied deep, deep, deep; In the soil they
sleep, sleep, sleep. Yel - low sun - beams bright, bright, bright;
C7
F
Rain-drops fall - ing light, light, light; Gen - tle breez - es
blow, blow, blow; Lit - tle seeds be - gin to grow.

Children like to interpret rhythmically the seeds growing, the sun shining, the rain falling, and the breeze blowing.

Springtime

Virginia Pavelko
Virginia Pavelko
Cheerily
F Bb F
The air is warm and the sky is blue The
C7 F G C
leaves are green yel - low be - cause they're new. Your
F Bb F
feet go skip - ping, the birds all sing, The
C7 F G C7 F
whole world is hap - py be - cause it is spring.

Fun on the Farm

If you would like to sing today
And want a few ideas,
Sing about a donkey
With big, long ears;
Sing about a mother hen,
A dairy and a cow;
Sing about a cornfield or a plow.
If you would like to sing today
Of animals or birds,
I'll listen as you make a tune
And choose your own words.

Gath'ring the Eggs

L. F. W. L. F. W.

Down on the farm, gath-'ring the eggs, Chas-ing a-way the old red hen,
How man-y eggs can you find? Two, four, six, eight, ten.

I'd Like To Be a Farmer

L. B. S. L. F. W.

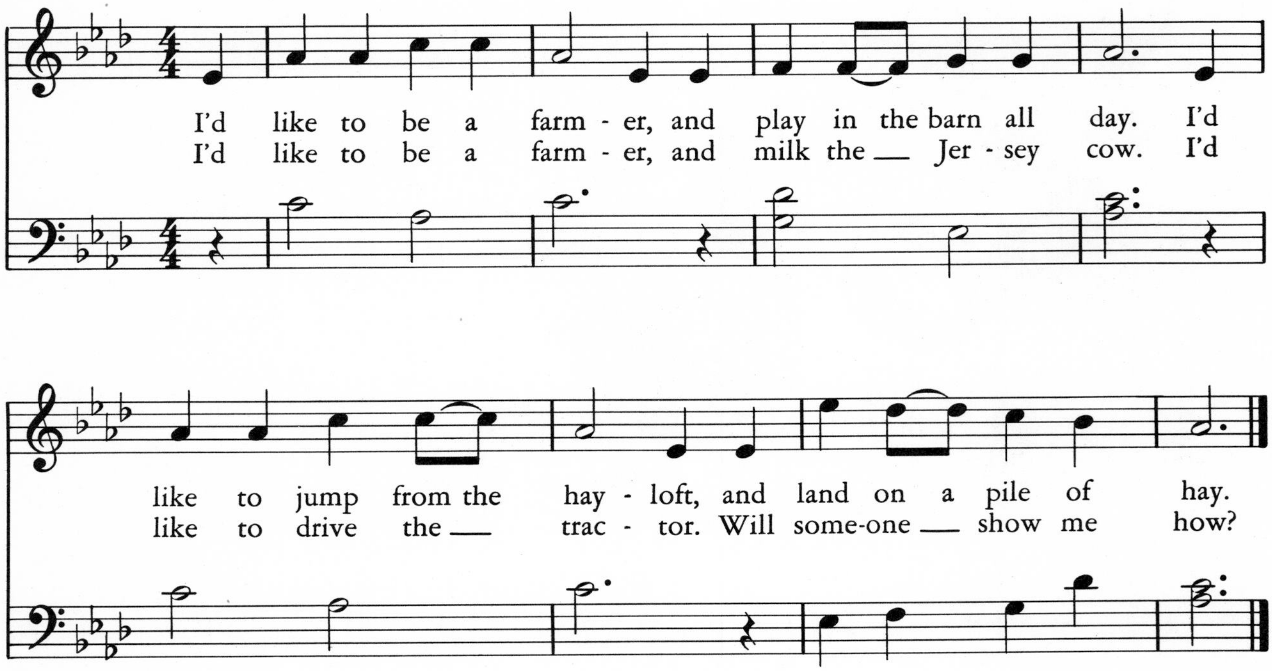

I'd like to be a farm - er, and play in the barn all day. I'd
I'd like to be a farm - er, and milk the — Jer - sey cow. I'd

like to jump from the hay - loft, and land on a pile of hay.
like to drive the — trac - tor. Will some-one — show me how?

The Little Red Hen

Adapted L. B. S.

L. F. W.

1. Who will plant this wheat? "I won't," Said the
6. Who will eat this bread? "I will," Said the
dog. "I won't," Said the cat. "I won't," Said the
dog. "I will," Said the cat. "I will," Said the
To be sung after the 6th verse
pig. "Then I will," Said the lit - tle red hen.
pig. "No, I will," Said the lit - tle red hen.
They would not help a
sin - gle bit, So the lit - tle red hen ate all of it.

2. Who will plow this wheat?
3. Who will thresh this wheat?
4. Who will grind this wheat?
5. Who will bake this bread?

My Pony

L. B. S. | L. F. W.

Galloping rhythm

G
Gal - lo - ping, gal - lo - ping, off we go, My

C | G
lit - tle black po - ny and I; ——

G
Gal - lo - ping on as I sing a song,

D7 | G
Yip - py aye Yip - py aye aye! ——

If You Were a Farmer

L. B. S. — Traditional

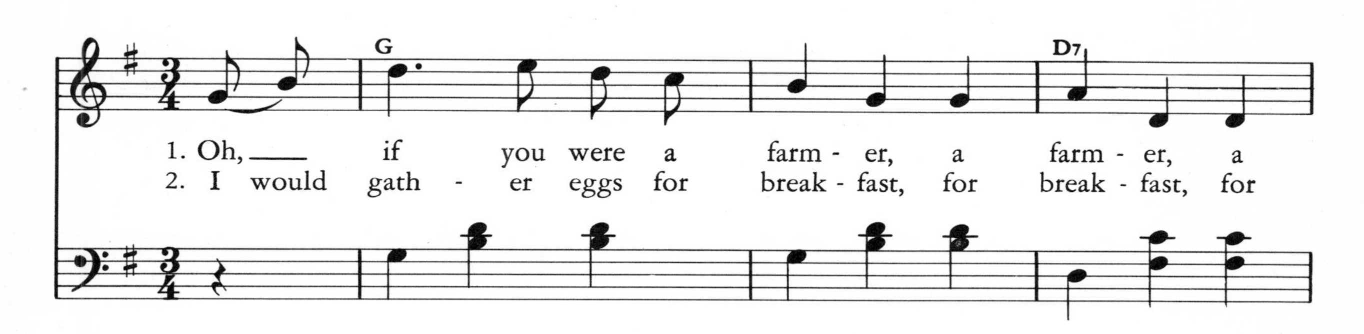
G
D7
1. Oh, if you were a farm - er, a farm - er, a
2. I would gath - er eggs for break - fast, for break - fast, for

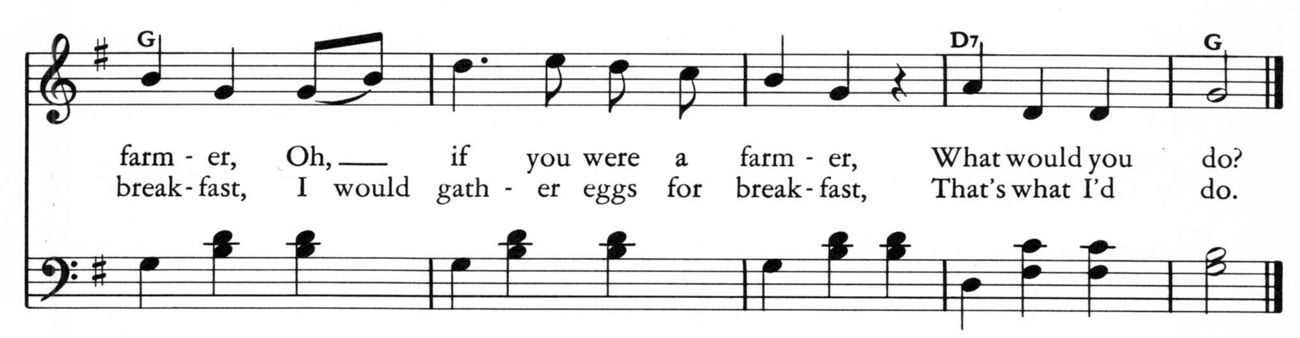
G
D7
G
farm - er, Oh, if you were a farm - er, What would you do?
break - fast, I would gath - er eggs for break - fast, That's what I'd do.

Verses may be added about other workmen like the fireman or the postman.

3. I would ride the cow to pasture.
4. I would milk the cow each morning.
5. I would feed the baby chickens.
6. I'd go plowing with a tractor.

The Singing Farm

L. F. W. L. F. W.

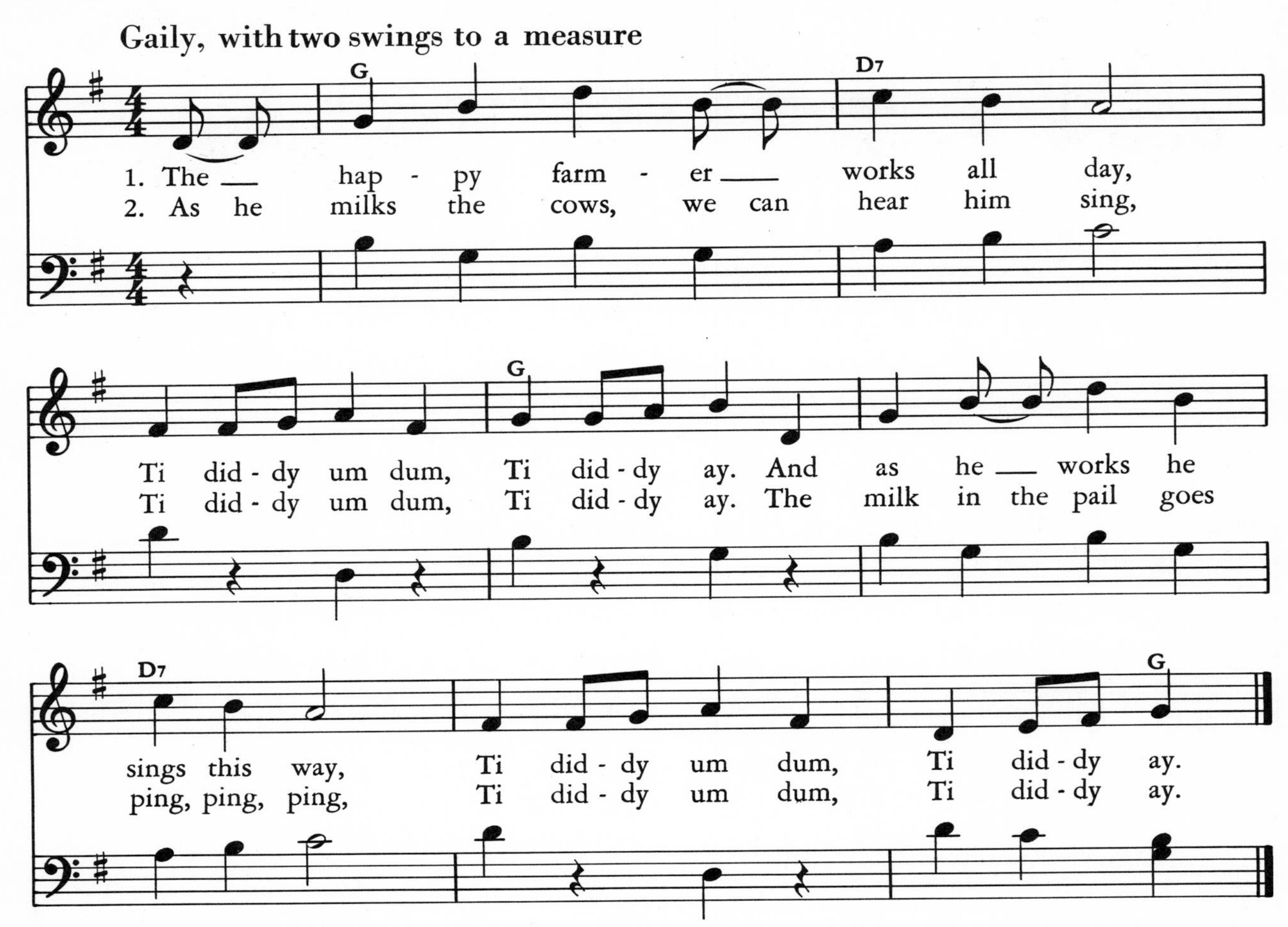

Gaily, with two swings to a measure
G
D7
1. The — hap - py farm - er — works all day,
2. As he milks the cows, we can hear him sing,
G
Ti did - dy um dum, Ti did - dy ay. And as he — works he
Ti did - dy um dum, Ti did - dy ay. The milk in the pail goes
D7
G
sings this way, Ti did - dy um dum, Ti did - dy ay.
ping, ping, ping, Ti did - dy um dum, Ti did - dy ay.

3. He sings so loud and he sings so long,
   Ti diddy um dum, etc.
   And all the animals learn his song.
   Ti diddy um dum, etc.

4. The horses sing with a hungry neigh,
   Ti diddy um dum, etc.
   They're waiting for their oats and hay.
   Ti diddy um dum, etc.

5. He feeds the pigs and the chickens, too.
   Ti diddy um dum, etc.
   The roosters join with a cock-a-doodle-doo.
   Ti diddy um dum, etc.

6. On a lazy summer afternoon
   Ti diddy um dum, etc.
   The hens all cackle with a merry tune.
   Ti diddy um dum, etc.

7. And when the evening sun goes down,
   Ti diddy um dum, etc.
   He takes his family into town.
   Ti diddy um dum, etc.

8. He gets up early when the sun is red.
   Ti diddy um dum, etc.
   He sings all day till it's time for bed.
   Ti diddy um dum, etc.

Three Little Ducklings

L. B. S. L. F. W.

Pad - dle, pad - dle, pad - dle, off they go,
Three lit - tle duck - lings all in a row. Pad - dle, pad - dle, pad - dle,
Quack, Quack, Quack, Off to the pond, a - round — and back.

Ten Yellow Chicks

L. B. S.
L. F. W.
F
C7
Five eggs and five eggs, that makes ten.
C7
F
Sit - ting on top is a moth- er hen. Crack - le, crack - le, crack - le,
C7
F
What do I see? Ten yel - low chicks, fluff - y as can be!

Let's Take a Ride

99

Let's take a ride on a big, red truck;
Let's take a ride on a streamline train;
Let's take a ride in an automobile;
Let's take a ride in an aeroplane.
Just anywhere that you want to go,
Any place you want to be.
Choose any way you want to ride,
And come along with me!

Little Engine

L. B. S. L. F. W.

G
D7
G
I think I can, I think I can, Oh click - e - ty clack - e - ty
I thought I could, I thought I could, Oh tick - e - ty tack - e - ty

D7
G
D7
G
clack, I think I can, I think I can, A - long my sil - ver track.
tee, I thought I could, I thought I could, And now just look at me!

Bradley: "If we play sand blocks and a triangle before we sing, it will sound like a real train starting."

A Big Truck

L. F. W. L. F. W.

Evenly
g min
I'm a great big truck and I huff and puff Pull - ing
I ___ car - ry milk that is fresh and sweet From the

D7
up a moun - tain road.
dair - y to the town.

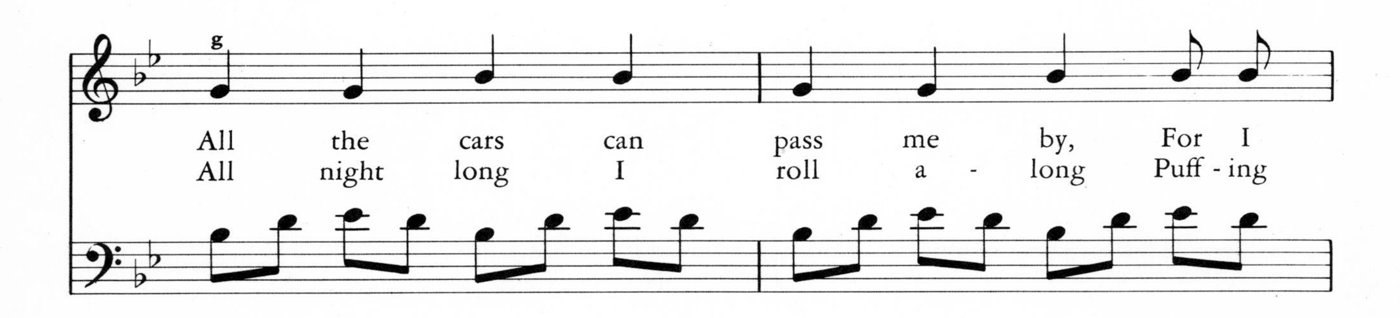
g
All the cars can pass me by, For I
All night long I roll a - long Puff - ing

D7
g
car - ry such a heav - y load.
o - ver the hills and down.

The children may want to make a verse about a different kind of truck.

My Rocket Ship

L. F. W. L. F. W.

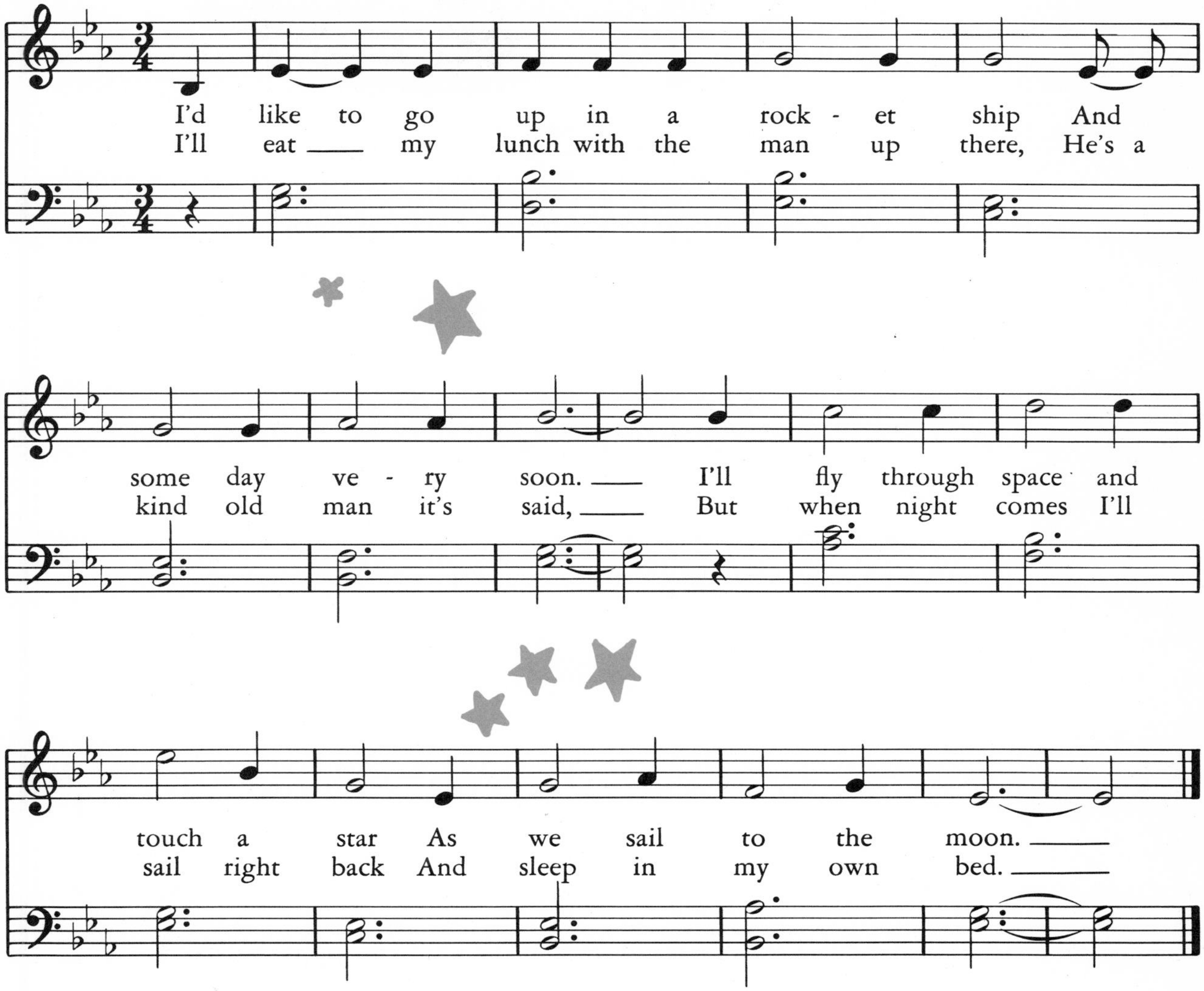

I'd like to go up in a rock - et ship And
I'll eat ___ my lunch with the man up there, He's a

some day ve - ry soon. ___ I'll fly through space and
kind old man it's said, ___ But when night comes I'll

touch a star As we sail to the moon. ___
sail right back And sleep in my own bed. ___

The Windshield Wiper

L. B. S. L. F. W.

Lightly

On Dad-dy's car the wind-shield wip - er goes ZH! ZH!

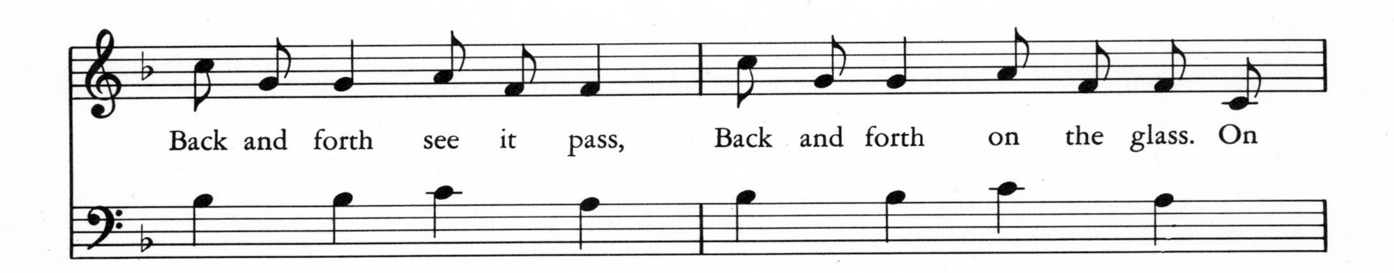
Back and forth see it pass, Back and forth on the glass. On

Dad - dy's car the wind - shield wip - er goes ZH! ZH!

My Family and My Town

Every day some people
Come to my house to call—
The mailman, the milkman,
And that isn't all;
The garbageman, the bakeryman,
The groceryman — oh, my!
So many, many people
Every day stop by.

Five Little Firemen

L. B. S. L. F. W.

Lively
Five lit-tle fire-men stand-ing in a row, 1, 2, 3, 4, 5, they go.
Hop on the en-gine with a shout, Quick-er than a wink the fire is out.

The Filling Station Man

L. B. S.

L. F. W.

G
The fill - ing sta - tion man is so po - lite, He
The fill - ing sta - tion man works oh, so hard. He

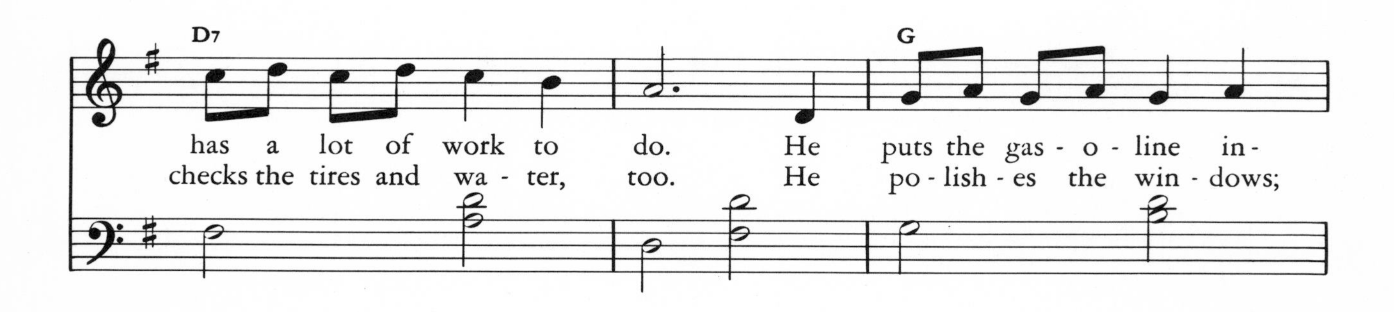
D7
G
has a lot of work to do. He puts the gas - o - line in -
checks the tires and wa - ter, too. He po - lish - es the win - dows;

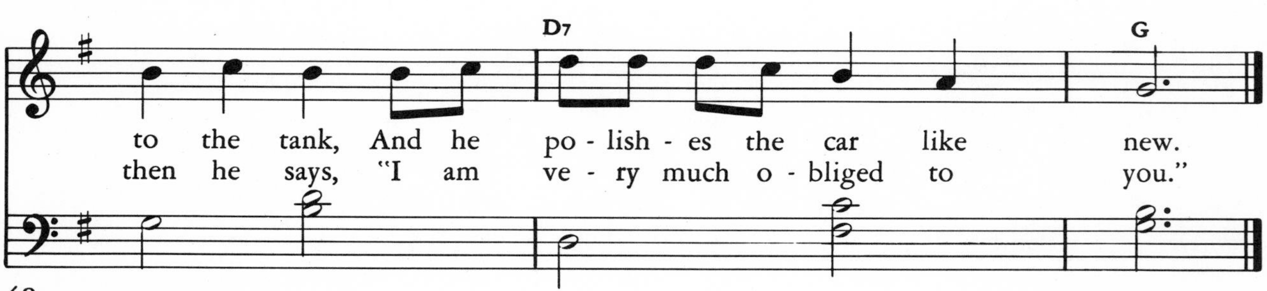
D7
G
to the tank, And he po - lish - es the car like new.
then he says, "I am ve - ry much o - bliged to you."

How Many People Live at Your House?

L. F. W.
L. F. W.
Lightly and gaily
How man - y peo - ple live at your house? How man - y peo - ple live at
your house? One, my fa - ther; two, my mo - ther; three, my sis ter;
four, my broth - er. There's one more, now let me see! Oh,
yes, of course it must be me! How man - y peo - ple live at
your house? How man - y peo - ple live at your house?

Policeman

L. B. S.
L. F. W.

Lightly
G
D7
Po - lice - man, Po - lice - man, How ve - ry tall you stand.
Po - lice - man, Po - lice - man, Would - n't it be grand If

G
All the cars will stop for you When you hold up your hand.
all the cars would stop for me When I hold up my hand?

Our Milkman

L. B. S. | L. F. W.

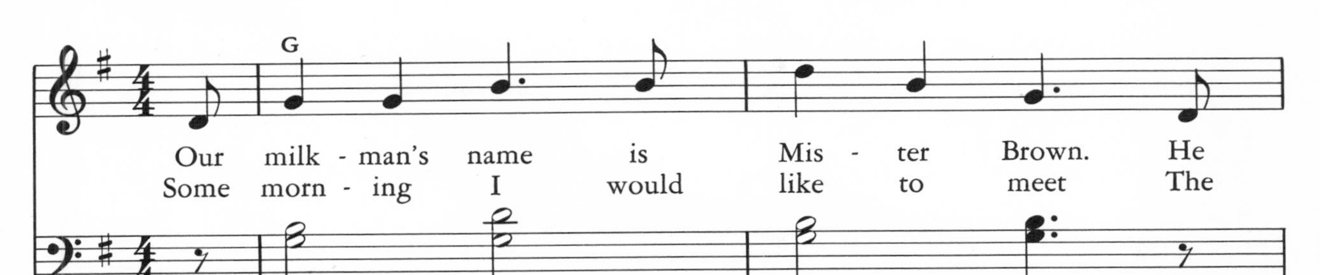
G
Our milk - man's name is Mis - ter Brown. He
Some morn - ing I would like to meet The

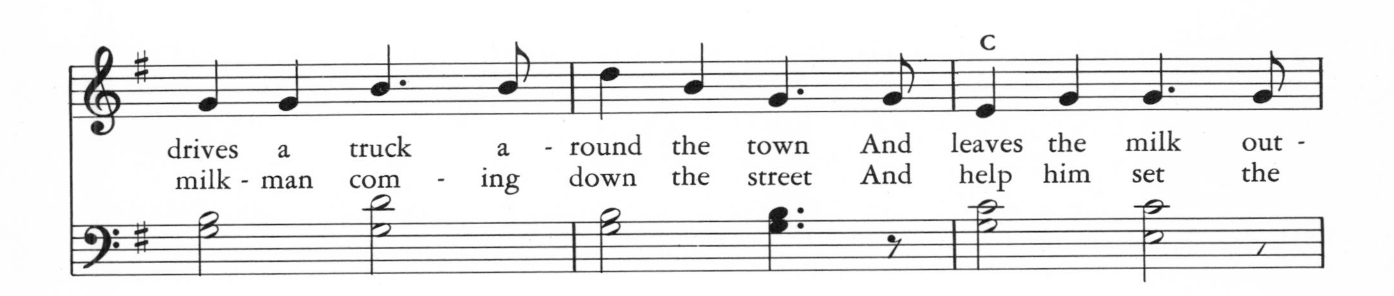
C
drives a truck a - round the town And leaves the milk out -
milk - man com - ing down the street And help him set the

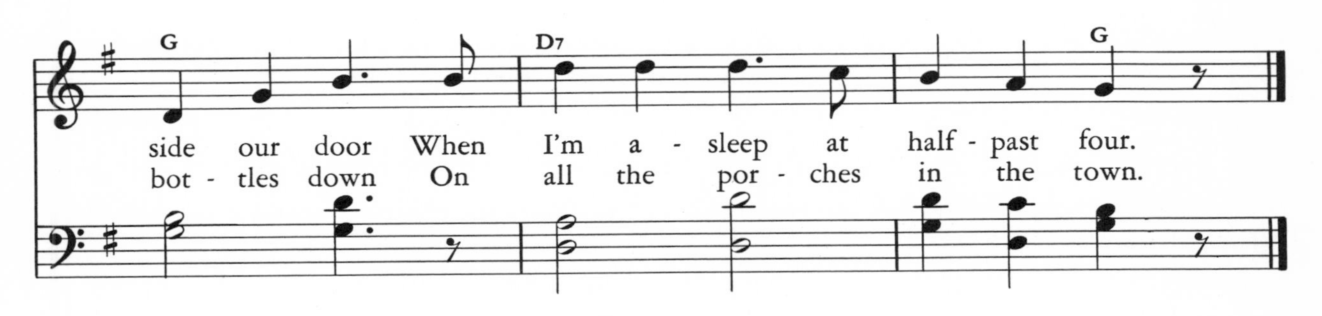
G
D7
G
side our door When I'm a - sleep at half - past four.
bot - tles down On all the por - ches in the town.

MILK

My Bugle

Virginia Pavelko
Virginia Pavelko
G
1. I want - ed a new bug - le so that I could blow and blow and blow. I
2. I want - ed a new drum to beat and go a march-ing down the street. I
D7
G
want - ed a new bug - le so my dad bought one for me. The
want - ed a new drum and so my dad bought one for me. The
C
G
D7
G
pup - py howled, the pus - sy yowled, the neigh-bors growled, my broth-er scowled, But
pup - py howled, the pus - sy yowled, the neigh-bors growled, my broth-er scowled, But
D7
G
when I play a bug - le call, They'll all be proud of me!
when I play a march - ing song, They'll all be proud of me!

The Bakery Truck

L. B. S. L. F. W.

If I could drive a bak - ery truck, At my house I would stop, — And

leave a choc - 'late birth - day cake, With frost - ing on the top! —
BAKERY

The Library Lady

L. F. W. L. F. W.

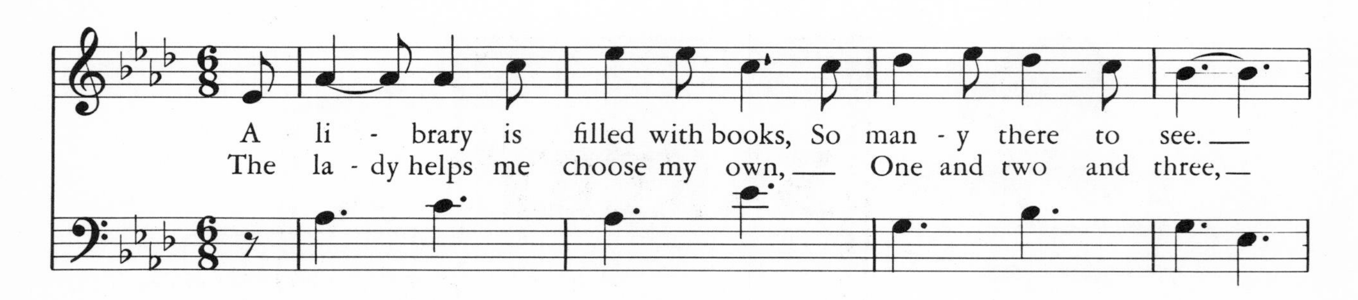

A li - brary is filled with books, So man - y there to see. —
The la - dy helps me choose my own, — One and two and three, —

Books for Mom-my and Dad - dy, too, And lots of books for me. —
Four and five — and six is all That she will lend to me. —

I'll Listen

L. B. S. L. F. W.

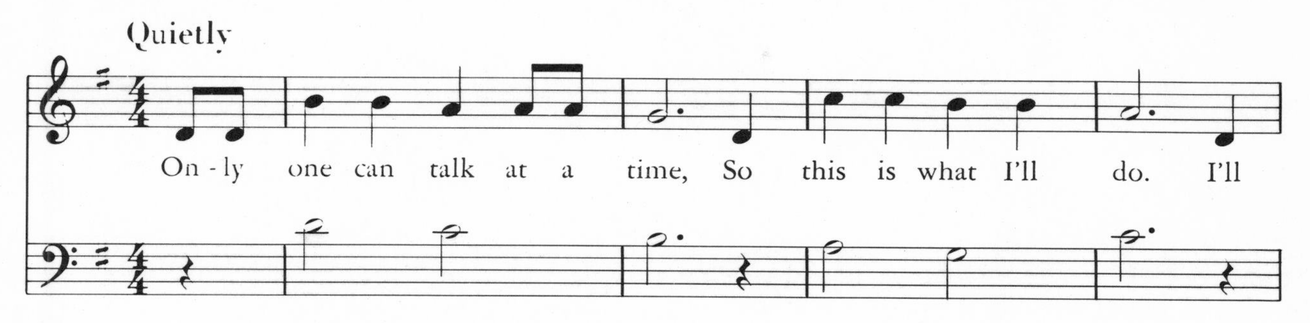
Quietly
On - ly one can talk at a time, So this is what I'll do. I'll

lis - ten still as a lit - tle mouse Till oth - er folks are through.

Ready to Listen

I'd like to be as sleepy still
As a fly perched on the window sill,
Or a pussy cat stretched out asleep,
Or a tiny fish in the ocean deep,
Or a flower petal blowing away;
But to BE still, I must FEEL that way.
I'll show you how quiet and still I can be
If you'll sing a sleepy tune to me.
A sleepy tune is the thing, you know,
To help me relax from head to toe.

I Wiggle

L. B. S. | L. F. W.

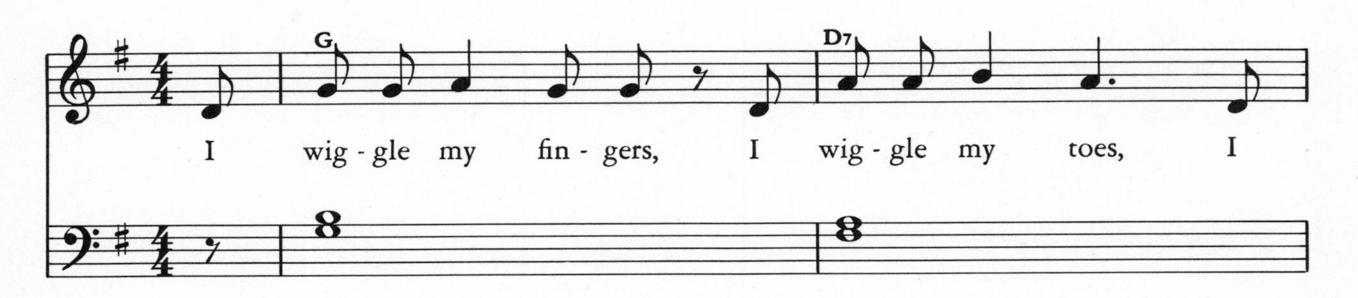
G
D7
I wig - gle my fin - gers, I wig - gle my toes, I

G
C
G
wig - gle my shoul - ders, I wig - gle my nose. Now, no more wig - gles are

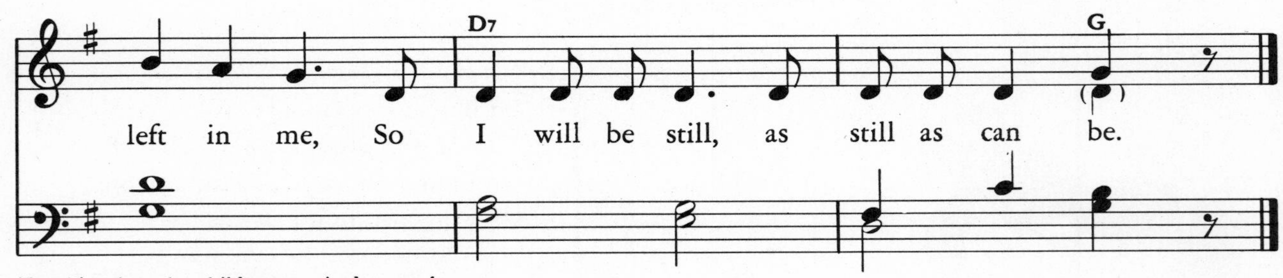
D7
G
left in me, So I will be still, as still as can be.

Try this when the children are tired or restless.

Jack-in-the-Box

L. B. S.
L. F. W.
Two swings in a measure
Jack-in-the-box, still as a mouse, Deep down in-side his lit-tle dark house.
Jack-in-the-box, rest-ing so still, Will you come out? Yes! I will!

My Hands

L. B. S. L. F. W.

Brightly
F
C7
F
My hands up - on my head I'll place, Up - on my shoul-ders, on my face.
F
C7
F
At my waist, and by my side, And then be - hind me they will hide. Then
B♭
F
I will raise them way up high, And let my fin - gers fly, fly, fly. Then
F
C7
F
clap, clap, clap and one, two, three, Just see how qui - et they can be.

This song is good for relaxation or for rainy day fun.

Two Little Hands

Unknown
L. F. W.
Lightly
G D7 G
Two lit-tle hands go clap, clap, clap. Two lit-tle feet go tap, tap, tap.
G D7 G
Two lit-tle hands go thump, thump, thump. Two lit-tle feet go jump, jump, jump.
G C G ritard D7 G D7 G
One lit-tle bo-dy turns a-round; One lit-tle child sits qui-et-ly down.

It is fun to find rhythm instruments that sound like the "claps," "taps," and "thumps."

Ten Miles from Home

Traditional

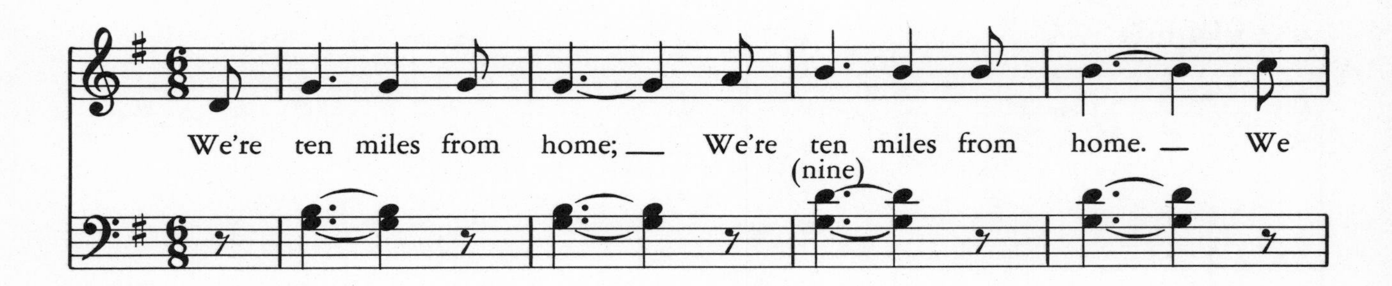
We're ten miles from home; We're ten miles from home. We
(nine)

walk a-while; we rest a-while; We're nine miles from home.
(eight)

Last verse ends with: "And now we are home."

Fun with Numbers

1, 2, tie your shoe.
3, 4, touch the floor.
5, 6, stir and mix.
7, 8, sit and wait.
9, 10, count again.
1, 2, 3, 4, 5, 6, 7, 8, 9, 10.

How Old Are You?

L. F. W. | L. F. W.

Tom - my, Tom - my, how old are you to - day? How

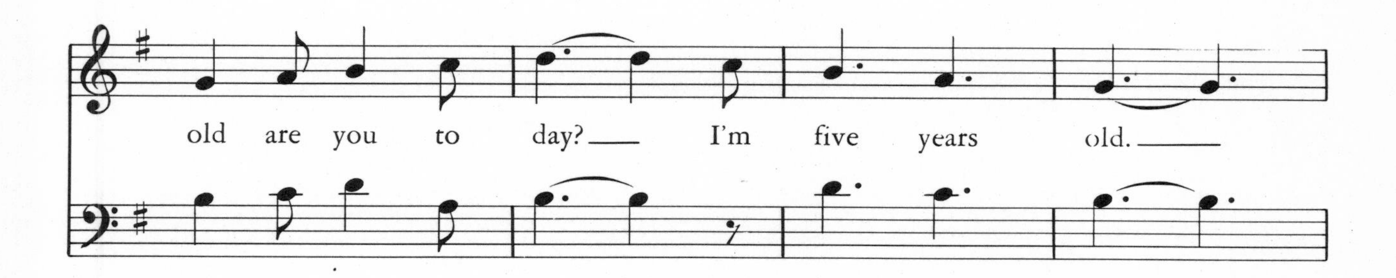
old are you to day? I'm five years old.

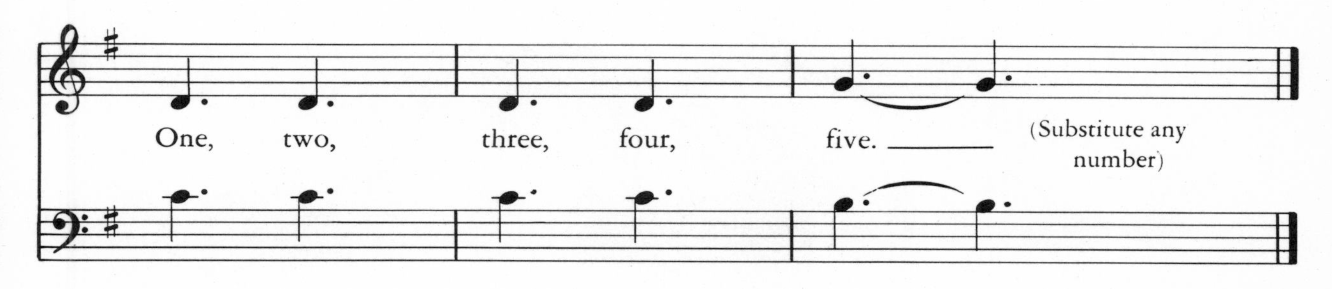
One, two, three, four, five.
(Substitute any number)

The Cuckoo Clock

L. B. S. L. F. W.

Accented

Tick - tock, Tick - tock, Hear the lit - tle cuck - oo clock.

Tick - tock, Tick - tock, Now he's call - ing four o' clock. Cuck -
(ten)

oo! Cuck - oo! Cuck - oo! Cuck - oo!

Marjorie: "If Susan plays the rhythm sticks on the *tick* and I play the wood block on the *tock*, it sounds like a real clock.

The Old Clock

L. F. W. L. F. W.

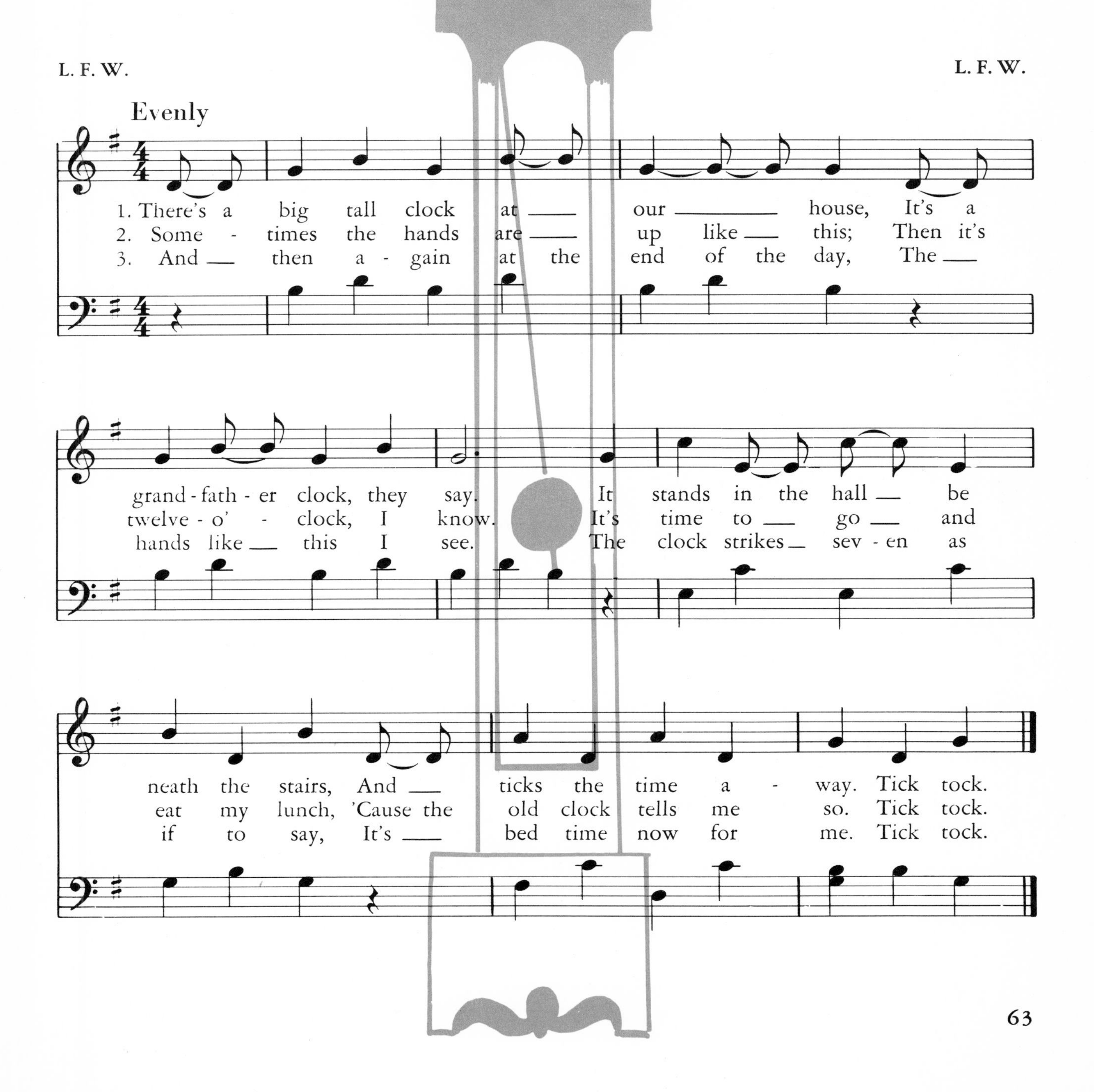
Evenly
1. There's a big tall clock at — our — house, It's a grand-fath-er clock, they say. It stands in the hall — be neath the stairs, And — ticks the time a - way. Tick tock.
2. Some - times the hands are — up like — this; Then it's twelve-o' - clock, I know. It's time to — go — and eat my lunch, 'Cause the old clock tells me so. Tick tock.
3. And — then a - gain at the end of the day, The — hands like — this I see. The clock strikes — sev - en as if to say, It's — bed time now for me. Tick tock.

Ten Little Frogs

L. B. S.

Virginia Pavelko

1. Ten lit - tle speck-led frogs, Sat on a speck-led log, Catch-ing some
2. Nine
most de - li - cious bugs, yum yum, One jumped in - to the pool, Where it was
nice and cool, And there were nine green speck-led frogs, glub, glub.
eight

Last verse:

One little speckled frog, Sat on a speckled log,
Catching some most delicious bugs, yum, yum,
He jumped into the pool, Where it was nice and cool,
And there were no green speckled frogs, glub, glub.

Circus Fun

Sing a song of circus time:
Wagons on parade,
Clowns with painted faces,
Sweet pink lemonade,
Horses white with ladies
Riding on their backs,
Lions, tigers, monkeys,
Seals all shiny black;
Elephants and camels
Slowly walk along.
Can't you see why CIRCUS
Makes the nicest song?

A Fat Hippopotamus

L. B. S.

L. F. W.

Ponderously
A fat, fat hip - po - pot - a - mus O - pened up his

jaw. He had the long - est, wid - est mouth I ev - er saw!

The Circus Is Here

L. B. S.
Esther Fahrney
Gleefully
The cir - cus is here! The cir - cus is here! To - day! To -
day! The cir - cus is here! The cir - cus is here! Hoo -
ray! Hoo - ray! There are li - ons and ti - gers and
mon - keys, you know There are ca - mels and pon - ies and

How about a circus parade on the lawn some day? Some children may play rhythm instruments with a march record for the circus band. The elephant's trunk can be old nylon stockings filled with newspapers. Someone might bring a wagon for the lion's cage.

el - e - phants Oh! The cir - cus is here! The cir - cus is here! To -
day! To - day! The cir - cus is here! The
cir - cus is here! Hoo - ray! Hoo - ray!

Circus Clown

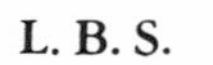

L. B. S. L. F. W.

Merrily

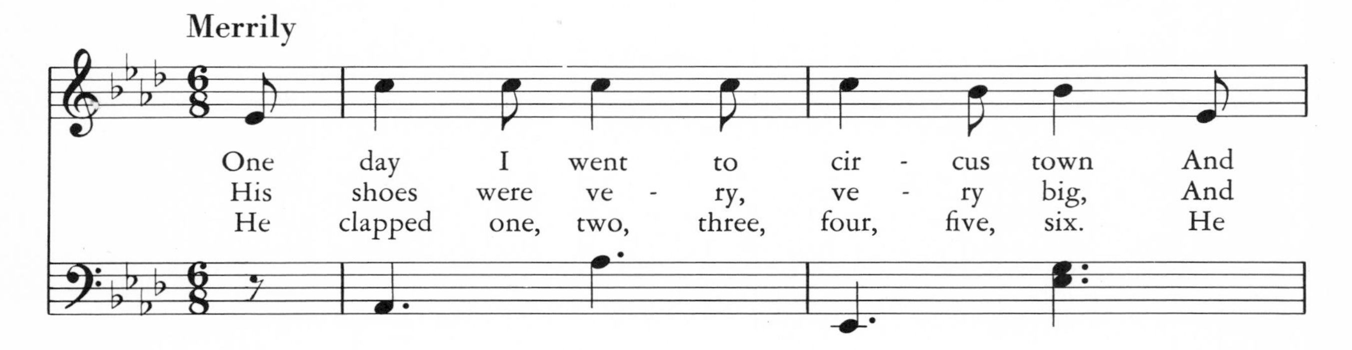
One day I went to cir - cus town And
His shoes were ve - ry, ve - ry big, And
He clapped one, two, three, four, five, six. He

saw a flop - py cir - cus clown. His face was paint - ed
on his head he wore a wig. His ears stood out, his
did some ve - ry fun - ny tricks, And then he tum - bled

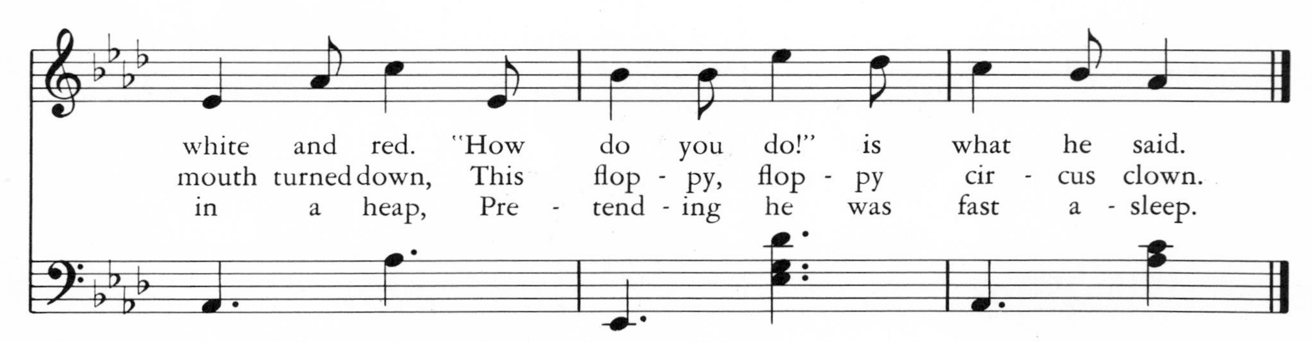
white and red. "How do you do!" is what he said.
mouth turned down, This flop - py, flop - py cir - cus clown.
in a heap, Pre - tend - ing he was fast a - sleep.

It is always fun to imitate the antics of a clown and clap on the last verse.

A Camel

L. B. S.
L. F. W.

Accented

I'd like to go o - ver the des - ert, Bump - i - ty,

bump - i - ty, bump,
Rid - ing on top of a

ca - mel's Hump - i - ty, hump - i - ty, hump.

A Seal

L. B. S. L. B. S.

The seal has flaps in - stead of toes, And

way up - on his tail he goes To catch a great big

strip - ed ball, And hold it on his nose.

The Giraffe

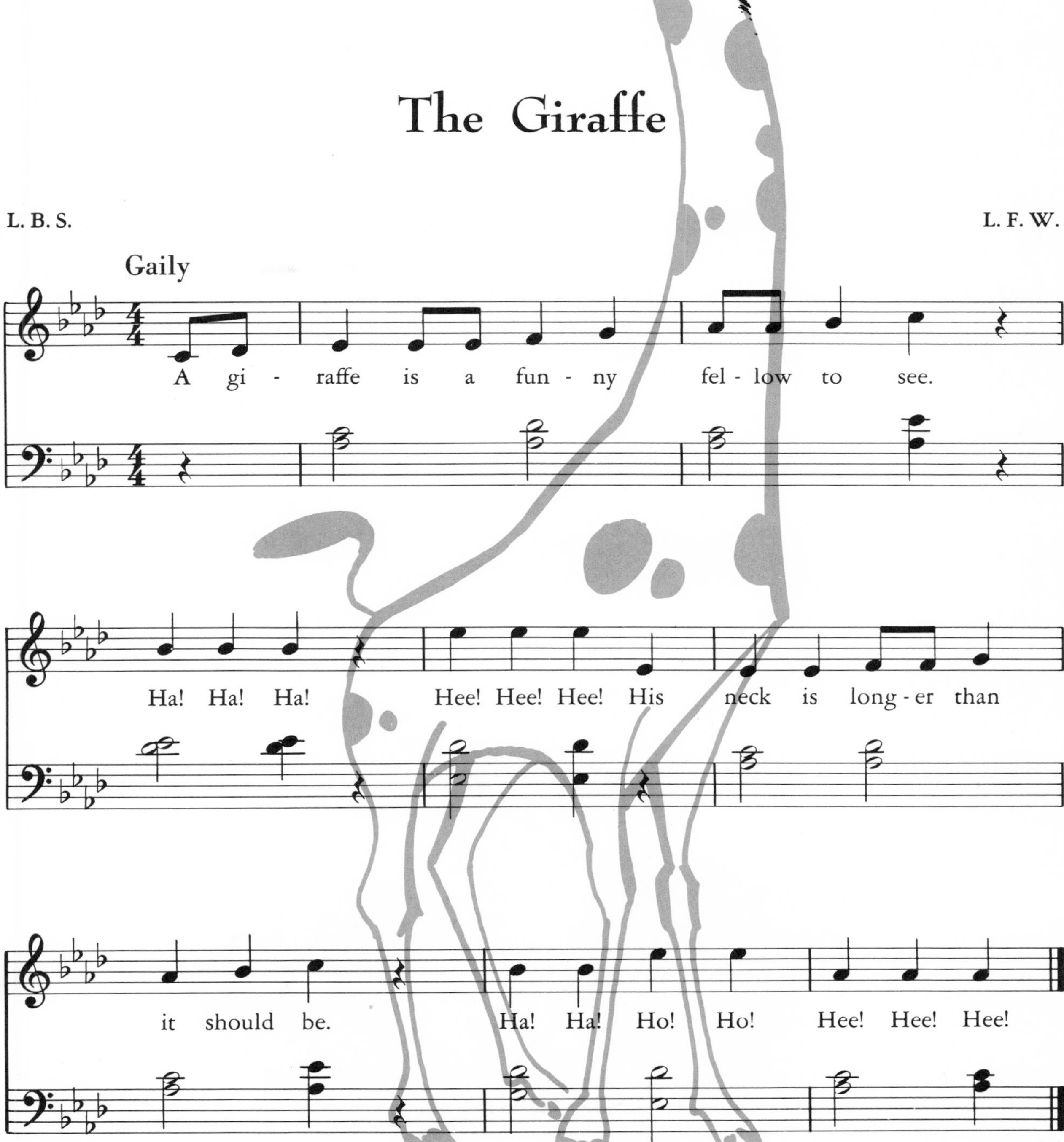
L. B. S.
L. F. W.
Gaily
A gi - raffe is a fun - ny fel - low to see.
Ha! Ha! Ha! Hee! Hee! Hee! His neck is long - er than

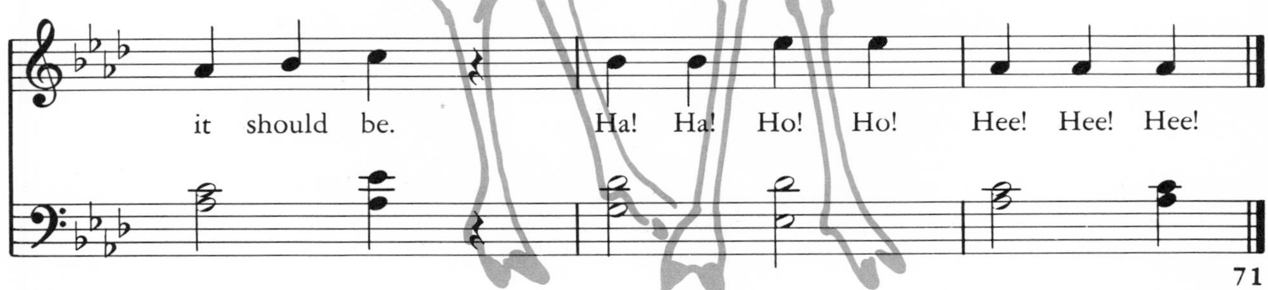
it should be. Ha! Ha! Ho! Ho! Hee! Hee! Hee!

My Puppet

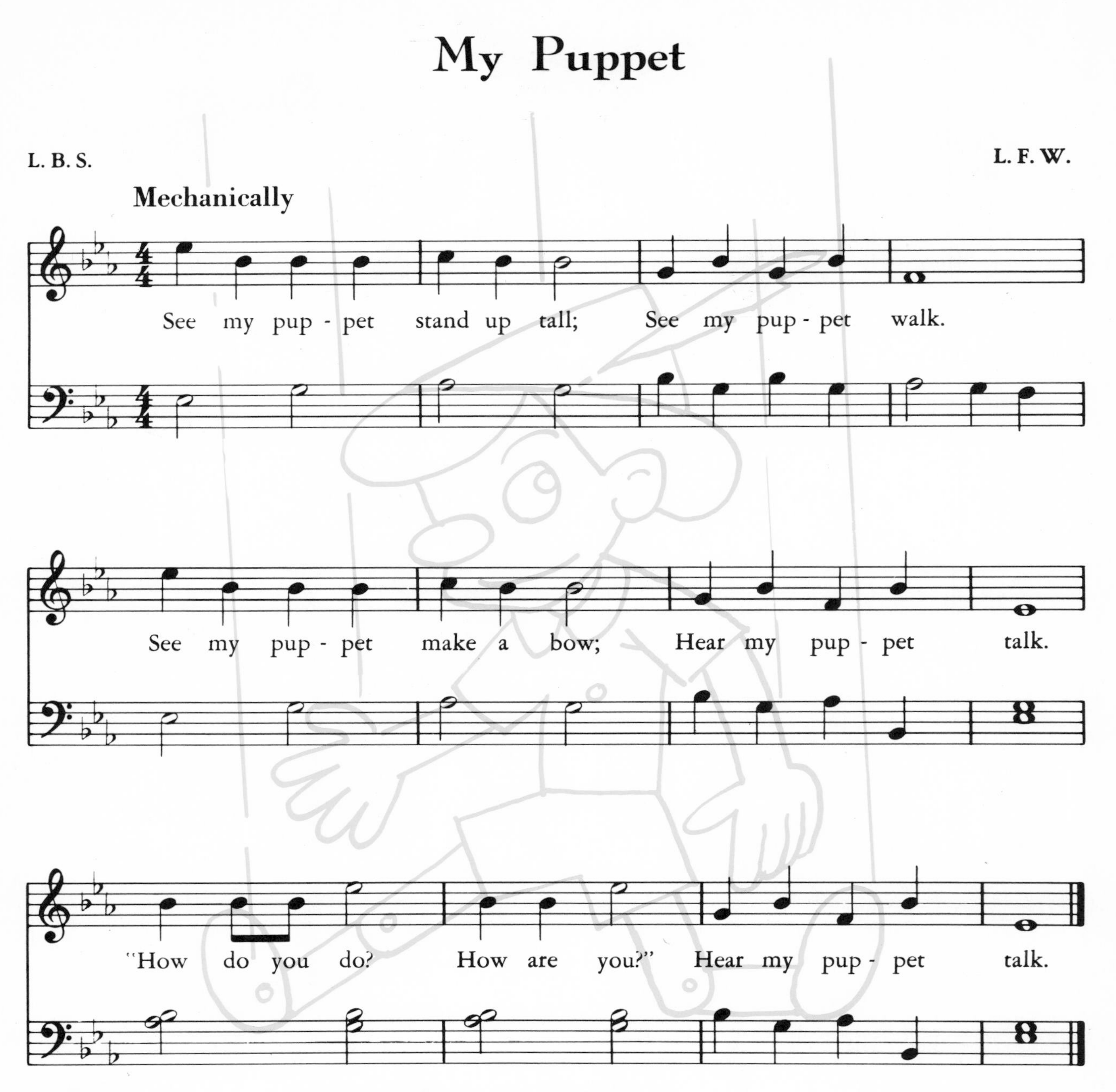
L. B. S.
L. F. W.
Mechanically
See my pup - pet stand up tall; See my pup - pet walk.
See my pup - pet make a bow; Hear my pup - pet talk.
"How do you do? How are you?" Hear my pup - pet talk.

Fun with My Fingers

Five little kittens playing by the door:
One chased a mouse and then there were four.
Four little kittens playing by the tree:
One chased a puppy; then there were three.
Three little kittens singing, "Mew, mew!":
One chased a bunny and then there were two.
Two little kittens having lots of fun:
One chased a butterfly; then there was one.
One little kitten resting in the sun:
He chased his tail and then there was none!

Eency, Weency Spider

Traditional

G
D7
G
Een - cy, ween - cy spid - er went up the wa - ter spout.
G
D7
G
Down came the rain, and washed the spi - der out.
G
D7
G
Out came the sun, and dried up all the rain, And the
G
D7
G
een - cy, ween - cy spid - er went up the spout a - gain.

The Little White Rabbit Who Wanted Red Wings

(A Folk Tale)

L. B. S. L. F. W.

CHILDREN: Everyone talks and everyone sings
Of the little white rabbit who wanted red wings.

READER: Once there was a little white rabbit. He had two long, pink ears. He had two red eyes. He had four soft feet. But the little white rabbit was sad. He wanted to be different.

CHILDREN: He wished to be a squirrel instead.
He twinked his nose and scratched his head,
And this is what he said:

RABBIT:

I wish to be a big, gray squirrel, And have a bush - y tail to curl.

CHILDREN: Old Mister Porcupine came by.
The little rabbit then did sigh:

RABBIT:

If I could have some bris - tles, oh, I'd be so hap - py then, I know.

CHILDREN: Little Miss Puddle Duck with a yellow back
Paddled along saying, "Quack, quack, quack!"

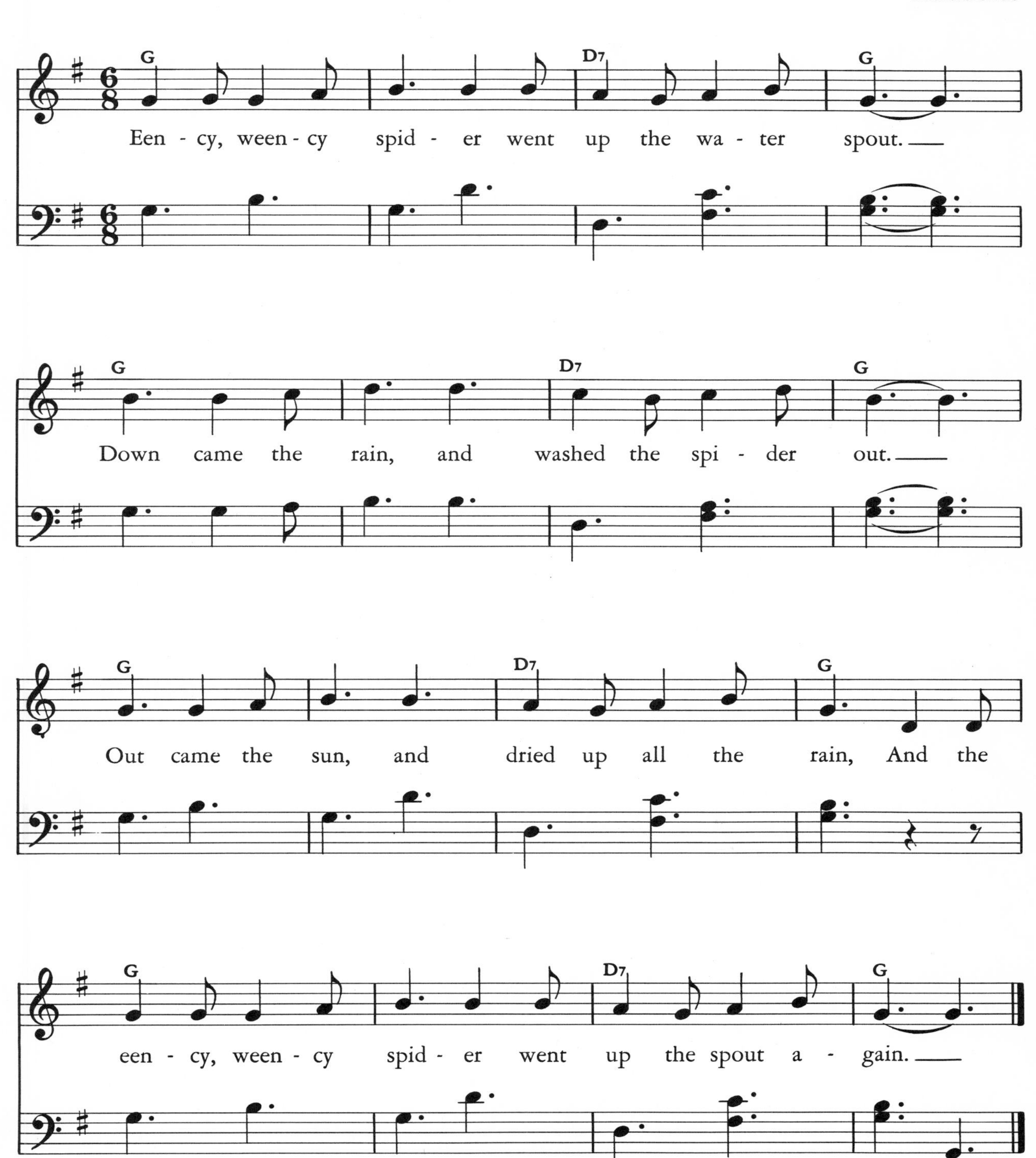

RABBIT:

I wish I had some rub-bers red, And yel-low feath-ers on my head.

READER: The little white rabbit wished and wished and wished. His mammy grew tired of his wishing. One day Mister Groundhog said to the little white rabbit:

GROUNDHOG: Go down to the wishing pond
By the old oak tree.

Turn around three times and wish;
Your true wish you will see.

READER: The little white rabbit went to the wishing pond. He saw a red bird drinking from the pond. He turned around three times and wished.

RABBIT:

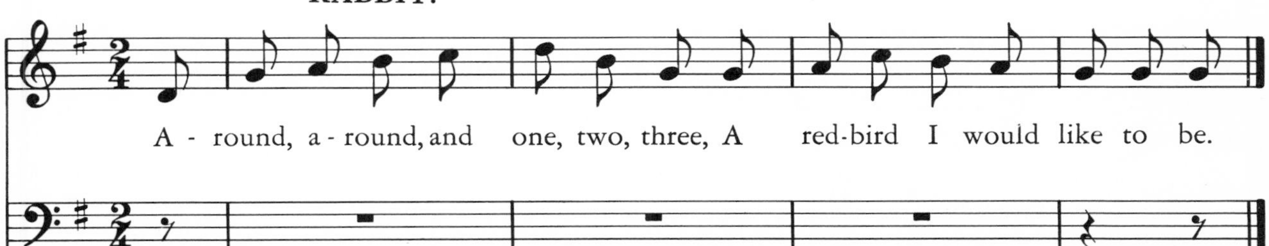
A - round, a - round, and one, two, three, A red-bird I would like to be.

READER: Then it happened! He began to feel something on his shoulders. It was wings coming through. The wings grew and grew. Soon they were full-grown red wings. The little white rabbit hopped home to show his mammy the red wings.

MAMMY: What is this? What is this?
Whatever can it be?
A rabbit with red wings cannot belong to me!

READER: The little white rabbit with red wings had to go away and look for a place to sleep. His mammy did not know him. She would not let him sleep in his own little bed. He went to the squirrel's house.

RABBIT:

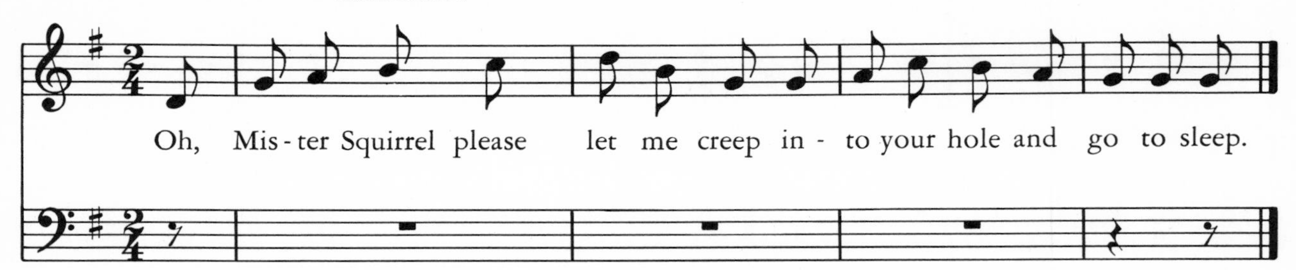
Oh, Mis - ter Squirrel please let me creep in - to your hole and go to sleep.

SQUIRREL: I do not know you. Go away!

CHILDREN: (slowly)
The little white rabbit with two red wings
Was sleepy as sleepy could be.
He came to the groundhog's house beneath
The friendly old oak tree.

READER: Mister Groundhog let the little white rabbit with red wings sleep on his floor all night. But the floor was covered with nuts and they made the little rabbit's feet hurt. In the morning, the little white rabbit spread his red wings. He tried to fly, but he landed in a bush. He could not get out.

RABBIT:

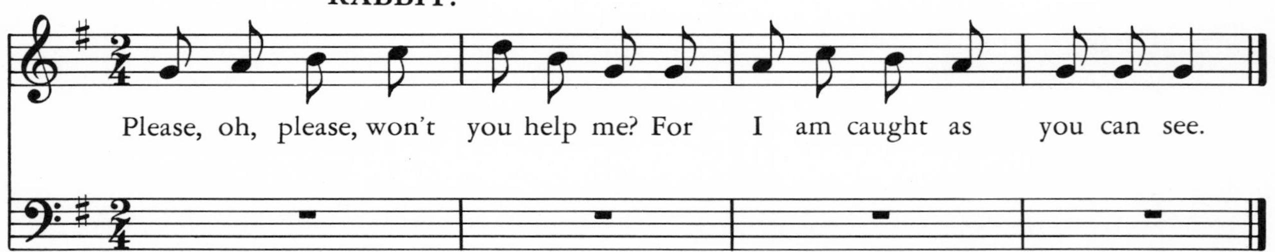
Please, oh, please, won't you help me? For I am caught as you can see.

GROUNDHOG: Did I hear somebody shout?

RABBIT:
Please, oh, please, won't you help me? For I am caught as you can see.

READER: Mister Groundhog helped the little white rabbit with red wings out of the bush. The little white rabbit did not want his red wings any longer. He did not know what to do. But Mister Groundhog was very wise. He told the little white rabbit to count to ten down at the wishing pond.

GROUNDHOG: Go down to the wishing pond and count to ten,
Turn around three times, and wish them off again.

READER: The little white rabbit did just that.

RABBIT:
Tick-tack-tee, ___ tick-tack-tee, My wings are gone and now I'm free.

CHILDREN: Hippety-hop, hippety-hop,
Back to his mammy without a stop.
Hippety-hop, hippety-hop,
She gave him a nice green carrot top.

READER: His mammy was SO glad to see him. And the little white rabbit never again wished to be anything different from what he was.

CHILDREN: Everyone talks and everyone sings
Of the little white rabbit who wanted red wings.

Contents

IT'S FALL

I'll Make a Scarecrow 1
Falling Leaves 2
The Owl and The Brownies 3
The Scarecrow 4
Little Jackie Jack Frost 5

HALLOWEEN FUN

Three Little Pumpkins 6
Halloween's Coming 7
I Made a Jack-O'-Lantern 8
In a Pumpkin Patch 9

LET'S PLAY INDIANS

Indian Chief 10
Indians in a Teepee 11
How Many Feathers? 12
Indians 13

THANKSGIVING TIME

Little Pilgrims 14
A Thanksgiving Prayer 15
Foolish Question 16
Three Turkeys 17

IT'S WINTER

The Snowman 18
I Am a Pine Tree 19
Walking Weather 20
Funny Little Snowman 21
Snowflakes 22-23
Ten Little Jingle Bells 24

CHRISTMAS TIME

Magic Time 25
Christmas Tree Angel 26
On a Christmas Night 27
Santa's Reindeer 28

IT'S SPRING

Easter Bunny 29
A Green Frog 30
My Easter Bonnet 31
Pussy Willow 32
Little Seeds 33
Springtime 34

FUN ON THE FARM

Gath'ring the Eggs 35
I'd Like To Be a Farmer 36
The Little Red Hen 37
My Pony 38
If You Were a Farmer 39
The Singing Farm 40
Three Little Ducklings 41
Ten Yellow Chicks 42

LET'S TAKE A RIDE

Little Engine 43
A Big Truck 44
My Rocket Ship 45
The Windshield Wiper 46

MY FAMILY AND MY TOWN

Five Little Firemen 47
The Filling Station Man 48
How Many People Live at Your House? . . 49
Policeman 50
Our Milkman 51
My Bugle 52
The Bakery Truck 53
The Library Lady 54

READY TO LISTEN

I'll Listen 55
I Wiggle 56
Jack-in-the-Box 57
My Hands 58
Two Little Hands 59

FUN WITH NUMBERS

Ten Miles From Home 60
How Old Are You? 61
The Cuckoo Clock 62
The Old Clock 63
Ten Little Frogs 64

CIRCUS FUN

A Fat Hippopotamus 65
The Circus Is Here 66-67
Circus Clown 68
A Camel 69
A Seal 70
The Giraffe 71

FUN WITH MY FINGERS

My Puppet 72
Eency, Weency Spider 73
The Little White Rabbit Who Wanted
Red Wings 74-77